they automatically close, you flick over our lines improving aerodynamics ActiveAerodynamics is just now available across the BMW range. Revolutionary cars with BMW EfficientDynamics.

BMW EfficientDynamics
Less emissions. More driving pleasure.

31 January call from Hard Rock Cafe® ✓
Pick up Jimi Hendrix's guitar from January's Best Hard Rock Cafe – Houston ✓
Package and pre-alert security through all gateways ✓
1 February deliver guitar to February's Best Hard Rock Cafe – Dublin ✓
Repeat every month of the year ✓

In the Hard Rock® world, DHL's Larry Casola
and his Express team – they rock ✓

www.dhl.com/larrycasola

DHL

NATIONAL GEOGRAPHIC

JUNE 2008 · VOL. 213 · NO. 6

CHROMODORIS SP.
STORY ON PAGE 92
PHOTO: DAVID DOUBILET

OFFICIAL JOURNAL OF THE NATIONAL GEOGRAPHIC SOCIETY

TALKING
EXPLORES HISTORY.
DOING
REWRITES IT.

IBM and National Geographic have teamed up on the Genographic Project – a five-year study that uses sophisticated computer analysis of DNA contributed by over 200,000 people to map how humankind has populated the globe and uncover the genetic roots we all share. Start seeing the bigger picture at ibm.com/dna STOP TALKING **START DOING**

Arctic Ocean

Honey's Healing Power

A Boon for Bonobos

On the Web

ngm.com

↘ Taking Stock of British Rocks
Try our Stonehenge quiz to see
if you know the real story behind
the mysterious slabs.

↘ All Over the Map
Our Map of the Day marks notable
moments, then and now: Ft. Sumter
surrenders, the Burma Road is
reopened, a man golfs on the moon.

On the Cover

The majesty and mystery
of Stonehenge still beckon.
Photo by Ken Geiger, NG Staff

⊕ Cover printed on recycled-content paper

Member Services

Customer Service
For subscriptions, gift
memberships, or changes of
address, contact customer
service at ngmservice.com,
or call 1-800-NGS-LINE
(647-5463). Outside the U.S.
and Canada please call
+1-813-979-6845. Write to
customer service at National
Geographic, PO Box 63001,
Tampa, FL 33663-3001.

Mailing List
We occasionally make
a mailing list available to
carefully screened com-
panies whose services may
be of interest to National
Geographic Society
members. To remove your
name from this list, email
ngsline@customersvc.com
or call 1-800-NGS-LINE
(647-5463). International

customers please
call +1-813-979-6845.
Or write: National
Geographic, PO Box 63005,
Tampa, FL 33663-3005.
Please include the
magazine address label.

Shopping
For National Geographic
products go to: shopng.com
or call 1-888-225-5647.

Online Index
For an online index of
all National Geographic
publications go to:
nationalgeographic.com/
publications.

Please Recycle This Magazine

Crested Capuchin *(Cebus robustus)*
Size: Head and body length, 33 - 50 cm; tail, approx. 45 cm   **Weight:** 2.0 - 3.8 kg
Habitat: Evergreen broadleaf rainforests and seasonal semi-deciduous forests of southeastern Brazil
Surviving number: Unknown, populations thought to be declining

SOUTH AMERICA
Atlantic Ocean
BRAZIL
Pacific Ocean

Photographed by Luiz Claudio Marigo

WILDLIFE AS CANON SEES IT

Smart. Tough. Resourceful. And disappearing. On the surface, the crested capuchin seems well suited for survival. Robust and exceptionally intelligent, it excels at adapting to new situations. One of the most omnivorous of the New World monkeys, it has learned to take what the forest offers: everything from seeds to small mammals. And the bands of 10 to 20 it lives in show considerable cooperation, with group members carrying and even suckling young other than their own. But its life is tied up in the trees, which are fast falling to farms, pastures and plantations. Vulnerable to hunting and the pet trade in its remaining redoubts, the crested capuchin proves that in today's world even the fittest may not survive.

As an active, committed global corporation, we join worldwide efforts to promote awareness of endangered species. Just one way we are working to make the world a better place—today and tomorrow. Visit **ngm.com/canonwildlife** to find out more.

EDITOR'S NOTE

In the photograph, a snow leopard emerges from the shadows of the rugged Himalaya. Its thick, soft coat is lovely, but even more enchanting is its tail. It is nearly the length of its body. This is my first opportunity to really study a snow leopard; I can see the rosette spots, penetrating yellow eyes, and broad, delicate paws. I've photographed leopards throughout Africa, but never one to match this creature's beauty. In a darkened room, Steve Winter shows his next photograph—

The snow leopard's long tail helps stabilize the cat on rough terrain.

another snow leopard, this one with a dusting of snow on its back. I read George Schaller's *Stones of Silence* 20 years ago and ever since have wanted to make a photograph like this. Schaller's book transported me to the Himalaya; I dreamed of seeing snow leopards at those heights. The dream remains unfulfilled, but for now Steve is there for all of us. His commitment to this beautiful animal has produced the finest images of snow leopards I've seen. But reality casts a shadow on these pictures. As few as 3,500 snow leopards may survive. If I want to photograph them, I should move quickly. Schaller's words still hold the same urgency they had nearly three decades ago: "The snow leopard," he wrote, "might well serve as symbol of man's commitment to the future of the mountain world."

PEOPLE BEHIND THE STORIES

■ **Roger Atwood**
Searching for "Afghanistan's Hidden Treasures," Atwood found in Kabul an unlikely

urban parallel. "I loved the stimuli of the Murad Khane neighborhood," he says. "The smell of cumin and curry, the twittering of caged birds, the booksellers and goat merchants and crowds of shoppers. The area is being restored now, but it was nearly demolished in the 1970s, a fact that reminded me of my hometown, Boston, and how much heritage we lost in misguided urban renewal plans around the same time. I'm fascinated by the life of great cities—the way they evolve over generations, their traditions, their resilience."

■ **Douglas H. Chadwick**
"There were times when I was simply struggling to breathe in that high, thin air, getting

beaten up by hailstorms or inching across cliff ledges with terrifying drops below," says Chadwick of his days and nights in the Himalaya searching for snow leopards. But the riskiest thing the prolific *Geographic* contributor did while writing "Out of the Shadows" had nothing to do with big cats or bad weather. "To be honest," he admits, "it was sitting on my rear end in various vehicles, dodging the untamed truck traffic that rampages along narrow highways full of hairpin turns."

INSPIRED BY THE PAST, BUILT FOR THE FUTURE.

LUMINOR MARINA.
Hand-wound mechanical movement
OP XI calibre. COSC certified.
Water-resistance 300 metres.
Steel case 44 mm Ø. Steel buckle.

PANERAI
LABORATORIO DI IDEE.

◻ NATIONAL GEOGRAPHIC

Inspiring people to care about the planet

The National Geographic Society is chartered in Washington, D.C., as a nonprofit scientific and educational organization "for the increase and diffusion of geographic knowledge." Since 1888 the Society has supported more than 8,000 explorations and research projects, adding to knowledge of earth, sea, and sky.

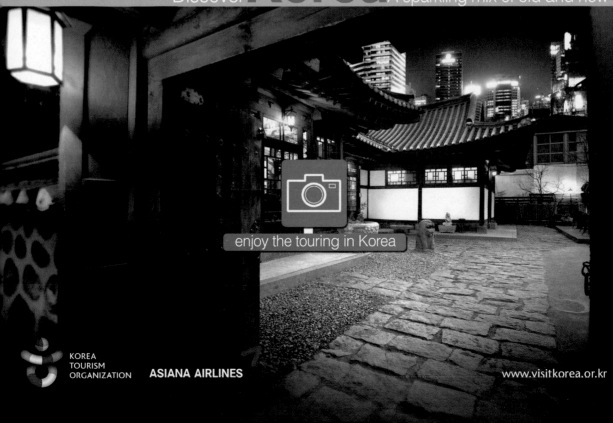

Korea **Sparkling**

enjoy the games in Beijing

90mins away from Beijing

Discover **Korea** A sparkling mix of old and new

enjoy the touring in Korea

KOREA
TOURISM
ORGANIZATION   **ASIANA AIRLINES**

www.visitkorea.or.kr

LETTERS

February 2008 *Our "Drying of the West" story drew a lot of mail this month. "Those living in the West should ask,"* wrote Craig Morgan of South Lake Tahoe, California, *"is it worth rolling up their lawns and fallowing their farmlands so that modern-day land barons can continue building more urban sprawl? Is this the civilization they desire?"*

➤ Comment on June stories at **ngm.com**.

Drying of the West

Your article talks about the tension between urban and rural water users as urban water managers take advantage of bought-up water rights, drill wells, and export water from rural aquifers. One source of this tension is the lack of consideration in how state and area water officials treat rural residents and their concerns of how water exportation from aquifers—relied on for our only source of water—affects wells. Consider this: When the water level of a particular aquifer drops to the point of being worthless to a user, the water authority simply moves on to the next aquifer, whereas rural residents are stuck with having to drill a new, deeper well or face the real possibility of having to pick up and move on if no more water is to be found. Water managers need to remember the primary rule of water rights. Mother Nature has no obligation to honor any man's water rights. When the water is gone, it's gone.

GREG GRIFFITH
Reno, Nevada

As conditions continue to worsen in the western states, I fear there will be more calls to tap the Great Lakes for water. This subject is raised often by government agencies and people who do not stop to realize the consequences. If the lakes were tapped and levels dropped, ships could no longer navigate the waterways. Hydroelectric generation would be curtailed or even finished at Niagara. Cities on the lakes such as Chicago and Toronto would have to spend millions to extend water intakes. Those western states had better start strict conservation programs and invest in research on improved desalinization projects.

KEN HEDGER
Goderich, Ontario

I suspect that the pool in the photo [pages 104-5] is actually an apartment-complex pool. The real irony of pools in the Phoenix area is precisely that they are not used by the density of people shown in the picture. If only they were, the water use would be more justified. The homes shown in the picture on page 113 are likely occupied by about three people. Most of those families will use their pool only a couple of times a week. Regardless of use, about one to two centimeters of water will evaporate every day during the five months of summer that we have in Arizona. In addition, the one-kilowatt pool pump must be run eight to twelve hours a day during the summer, and four to eight hours during the winter to keep the water filtered and clean. Unused pools do not just waste water; they waste energy too.

LANCE C. LABUN
Tempe, Arizona

Robert Kunzig's otherwise excellent article was marred by one jarring description that added nothing to his narrative and was remarkable only for its incongruousness. I refer to the description of the Southern Nevada Water Authority's Pat Mulroy as a "crisp, tanned, fiftysomething blonde with a tailored look and a forceful personality." It is notable that no other human being in the article is described by his or her appearance. At least one-half of your readership could live without the disappointing experience of being reminded, yet again, that its most notable attributes are cosmetic. For your information, what you probably want to know about me is that I am a petite, bespectacled brunette who would really appreciate being able to pick up your magazine without preparing for a possible gratuitous, subtle insult.

JUNE LEHRMAN
Culver City, California

Write, Email, Fax

Write
National Geographic Magazine
PO Box 98199
Washington, DC 20090-8199

Email
ngsforum@nationalgeographic.com

Fax
202-828-5460
Include name, address, and daytime telephone. Letters may be edited for clarity and length.

Emirates

1,100 hours of entertainment.

Emirates ice. The largest selection of inflight
movies, music and communication.

We all have our own idea of entertainment. That's why
Emirates ice has all the latest movies, TV series, chart topping
music, games, news reports, email, SMS messaging and a
phone at every seat. So you can tune in to whatever you want.

Fly Emirates. Keep discovering.

emirates.com

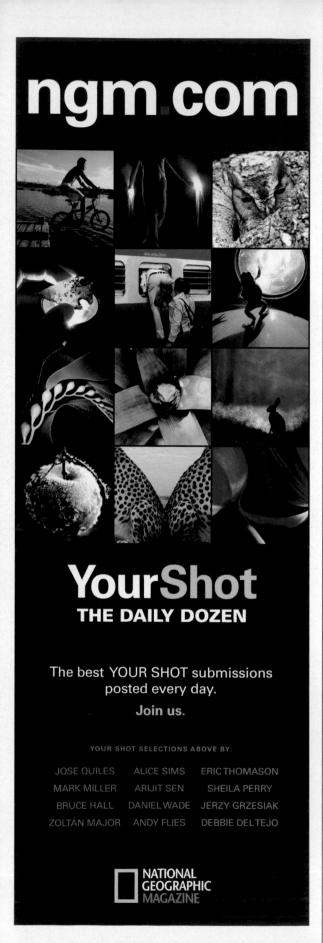
LETTERS

With increasing consumption and a higher likelihood of intense droughts, there will be some hard decisions to make regarding water use in the future. One user that needs further mention is the environment, which competes for scarce resources alongside cities and agriculture. This is seen in the Colorado River Delta (CRD), which is less than 10 percent of its original size and is sustained by agricultural runoff and municipal wastewater. The CRD was once a rich habitat for wildlife and indigenous people, but after damming and diverting the river, which started in the 1930s, the CRD began to lose its lifeblood. This is not to say that the water has not been put to important uses; it irrigates 3.5 million acres and quenches the thirst of 30 million people. However, there are ways to support the CRD while balancing other water uses.

KAREN HYUN
Washington, D.C.

On the Trail of a Ghost
I thought the author might have cited a haiku that Basho wrote after losing his house to fire. It is my favorite: "My house burned down. / Now I can better see / The rising moon."

CHARLES GARY SIGNOR
Harrisburg, Pennsylvania

Though this haiku is often attributed to Basho, experts we've consulted cannot find it in his writing. It may be by Masahide, a contemporary of Basho.

Corrections, Clarifications

February 2008:
Drying of the West The map on page 101 misplaced Albuquerque, New Mexico, and omitted Santa Fe. Ponderosa pine seeds were incorrectly described as wingless on page 102; they do have small wings.

On the Trail of a Ghost The birds flying across the map of Japan on page 140 are whooping cranes, native only to North America.

I was profoundly impressed by the 90-degree shift in format used for "On the Trail of a Ghost." It added force to Michael Yamashita's already powerful photography and allowed Howard Norman's text to be artfully displayed with the creative use of calligraphy. Having to hold and look sidelong at the issue was a novelty.

DONALD W. JOHNSTON
Oklahoma City, Oklahoma

What possessed you to print the article on the haiku master sideways? It was definitely a bad decision. It made the article totally unreadable in this household.

MARY ZELLE
Hixson, Tennessee

Thank you for the beautiful interpretation of Matsuo Basho. I was very impressed by its unique horizontal format, combined with exquisite photographs and elegant Japanese calligraphy. The first haiku, "…a frog jumping into a pond," is widely known in Japan. However, I was startled that the character for "frog" is missing from the calligraphy on page 145. Did the character disappear into the water?

KYO TAKAHASHI
Roscommon, Michigan

We regret that a production error caused Basho's frog to jump right off the page. Here is the poem in its entirety:

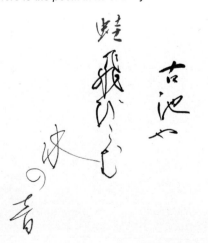

*N*ever met a diamond she didn't like

is an intrepid traveller

loves when the chef makes chateaubriand for her while staying at

The Fairmont Acapulco Princess

LaDonna – Fairmont guest since 1985

everyone's an original

HOTELS & RESORTS

africa • asia • bermuda • canada • caribbean • europe • united states • mexico | united arab emirates

contact your travel consultant, visit www.fairmont.com or call Fairmont at 00 800 0441 1414

LETTERS

Black Pharaohs

The article shows African people to be more than just a group exported as slaves to foreign lands. It shows the rise of African leadership in a region that dominated much of the ancient world: Egypt. All we can hope is that history books will be rewritten so that our children will learn the truth of our history and that all people, regardless of race, skin color, or culture, made an equally significant impact on our world.

WINSOME LORAINE PETER
Beijing, China

Serious academic attention to the Nubian pharaohs has been long overdue and certainly hampered by the construction of the Aswan High Dam. The disregard for this period of Egyptian history was only amplified starting in 1959, when an international team made extraordinary efforts to relocate the temples of Ramses II at Abu Simbel to protect them from the same rising waters that covered critical areas of Lower Nubia. And now another dam threatens our further uncovering of this great civilization. So what exactly have we learned from history?

KEITH NEMLICH
Manchester Center, Vermont

Actually, weren't all the pharaohs black? The ancient Egyptians claimed they migrated to Egypt from Ethiopia. What color are the folks in Ethiopia? Herodotus, in a roundabout way, stated the Egyptians had dark skin and hair "like wool." Look at the mask of Tutankhamun. Does he look like someone from Nairobi or Paris or Riyadh? The only reason ancient Egyptians are portrayed as nonblack is that when Egyptology started, white people were enslaving black people and justified it by claiming that blacks were inferior. This wouldn't hold water if people realized that there had been a black civilization that the ancient Greeks had borrowed many of their ideas from.

RICK POTTHOFF
Houston, Texas

Deep Thoughts Mysterious pictures of watery scenes inspired both the Your Shot editors and online voters this month. Now you can decorate your computer desktop with wallpaper of Your Shot photographs by choosing from our Daily Dozen top shots available for download. Get guidelines for sending in your own pictures, a submission form, and more information at *ngm.com/yourshot.*

Ashish Dubey Indore, India

Bent reeds mirrored in the surface of a lake looked like modern art to Ashish Dubey, a 44-year-old college physics teacher. He shot this at sunrise on Sirpur Lake, a favorite local landing spot for migratory birds.

Finn Müller Amsterdam, Netherlands

Somewhere on the road to Cape York, Australia, photography student Finn Müller, 24, saw this stranded tree. "The tree was not growing on an island, from what I could see. It was just standing there in the water," he says. This picture was voted an *ngm.com* audience favorite.

Nikon

At the heart of the image

Stunning photography is just a step away.

10.2 MEGA PIXEL

SMALL SIZE
BIG PERFORMANCE

Nikon
D60

Integrated Dust Reduction System – the advantage is clear.

The new D60 packs a world of creative features into its compact, lightweight body. But its most striking feature is one you'll never see. To prevent unsightly marks spoiling your images, the D60 is equipped with technology that uses ultrasonic vibrations to remove stray dust particles on the camera sensor. These particles are then disposed of by means of a controlled airflow system so you reduce the risk of getting marks on your images from the moment you switch the camera on. **D60: it's not just a camera. It's a Nikon.**

EXPEED

Take the next step at **www.europe-nikon.com**

These guns in Pyongyang were props—perhaps for a drill—but they reflect North Korea's military mind-set.

Yannis Kontos is a photographer for the Polaris Images agency. More of his work is online at yanniskontos.com.

Arm's Length I used to dream about seeing North Korea, the militantly communist Hermit Kingdom that few outsiders get to visit. Unfortunately, North Korea didn't want to see me. For three years I tried—and failed—to get a journalist visa, so I traveled as a tourist instead, flying to Pyongyang with a small, state-sanctioned group led by government-appointed guides. Since visitors are forbidden to carry professional cameras (photography, in general, makes officials nervous), I packed two small, amateur models. When I used them, I often shot from the hip—literally—snapping pictures without looking through the viewfinder. Every night at the hotel I'd download my photos to an MP3 player while my roommate slept. Sometimes I felt like a spy. Other days I felt like an extra on a huge movie set, where citizens were the actors, and the director hovered somewhere in the shadows, making sure we stuck to the script.

I wasn't surprised by the nation's story line—the revolutionary passion, the emphasis on ethnic purity, the near deification of the "Great Leader," Kim Il Sung (1912-1994), and the reverence for his son, the "Dear Leader," Kim Jong Il. But I didn't expect North Koreans to be so happy. They waved at me. They smiled. They seemed unfazed by—or unaware of—how the world perceived their country. Sure, maybe that's part of the performance, but it's tough to tell. I couldn't ask provocative questions, and most people were afraid to talk. While I managed to capture some hidden corners of this country, it was the eerie silence that really opened my eyes.

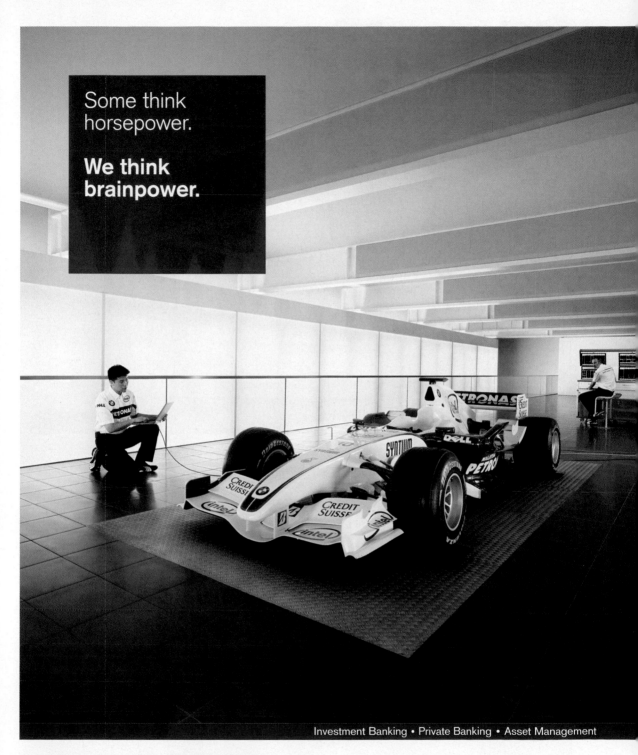

Some think
horsepower.

**We think
brainpower.**

Investment Banking • Private Banking • Asset Management

We look at things from a different perspective – for the
benefit of our clients. Building on our experience and
expertise to drive innovation is an approach we share
with the BMW Sauber F1 Team. By challenging
conventional thinking we help our clients realize new
opportunities. This has been our ambition since 1856.
www.credit-suisse.com/sponsoring

Thinking New Perspectives.

CREDIT SUISSE

One evening at the Yanggakdo Hotel in Pyongyang, I saw these men playing billiards. They're probably hotel workers, because most of the guests are either tourists or Chinese businessmen. The hotel keeps visitors on a tight leash; there's nothing to do at night anyway, even if you were allowed to go out.

There's no escape from all the political art in Pyongyang, including this 160-foot-high hammer, sickle, and brush built in 1995 to celebrate the 50th anniversary of North Korea's Workers' Party. Communism may be on the wane elsewhere, but giant statuary serves as a potent reminder to the people: The state is far bigger than you are.

Hidden talents

Behind the mask of point-and-shoot simplicity, lies a camera of extraordinary capability. One that gives you all the confidence to explore those creative talents you maybe never realised you had. Beautifully built, with a specification that outstrips anything else in its class, the K20D could well be the key to revealing the true you.

It's pure Pentax!

- Low noise 14.6 megapixel CMOS sensor
- Large Live-View LCD screen
- In-camera Shake Reduction with any Pentax K Lens
- Four stage dust protection system
- Fully sealed dust and water resistant body
- Dynamic Range Enhancement
- 14-bit D/A converter

www.pentax.co.uk

K20D

PENTAX

As our train clattered through a station not far from the capital, I secretly snapped this shot. Who are these men? Maybe they're railway workers on a break. Maybe not. I didn't dare ask. Too many questions would arouse suspicion. As a result, many of my pictures remain enigmatic to me—like a silent movie without subtitles.

Lush crops line this stretch of track, but on a train trip across the countryside, another truth emerged: Most farmers lash plows to animals, not tractors, and cut their fields with scythes. North Korea's fuel crisis keeps them from using what machinery they have. The country depends heavily on foreign food aid to avert widespread hunger.

CHINA

LIQUORICE

CORIANDER, *Morocco*

BOMBAY
SAPPHIRE
Distilled
LONDON
DRY GIN

*Distilled from 100%
Grain Neutral Spirit
from a 1761 recipe*

THE BOMBAY SPIRITS COMPANY,
London 1820 1931
PRODUCT OF ENGLAND
PREMIUM

PREMIUM

Juniper and Iris root, Italy

Behind Every Treasure
Is An Intriguing Story.

Fresh from Morocco, coriander seeds add hints
of spice, lemons and oranges, which through
vapour infusion, help create the crisp,
delicately balanced taste
of Bombay Sapphire.

New York City Secret prize on the urban game board, a miniature garden brightens a Rockefeller Center rooftop seven stories above midtown traffic. Four gardeners labor eight hours a week to keep its lawn and hedges trim.

Arctic Ocean The 22-ton stainless steel propellers on the icebreaker *Louis S. St-Laurent* pause in their work pushing the Canadian vessel through frozen waters—allowing a diver to venture near.

PHOTO: PAUL NICKLEN, NATIONAL GEOGRAPHIC IMAGE COLLECTION

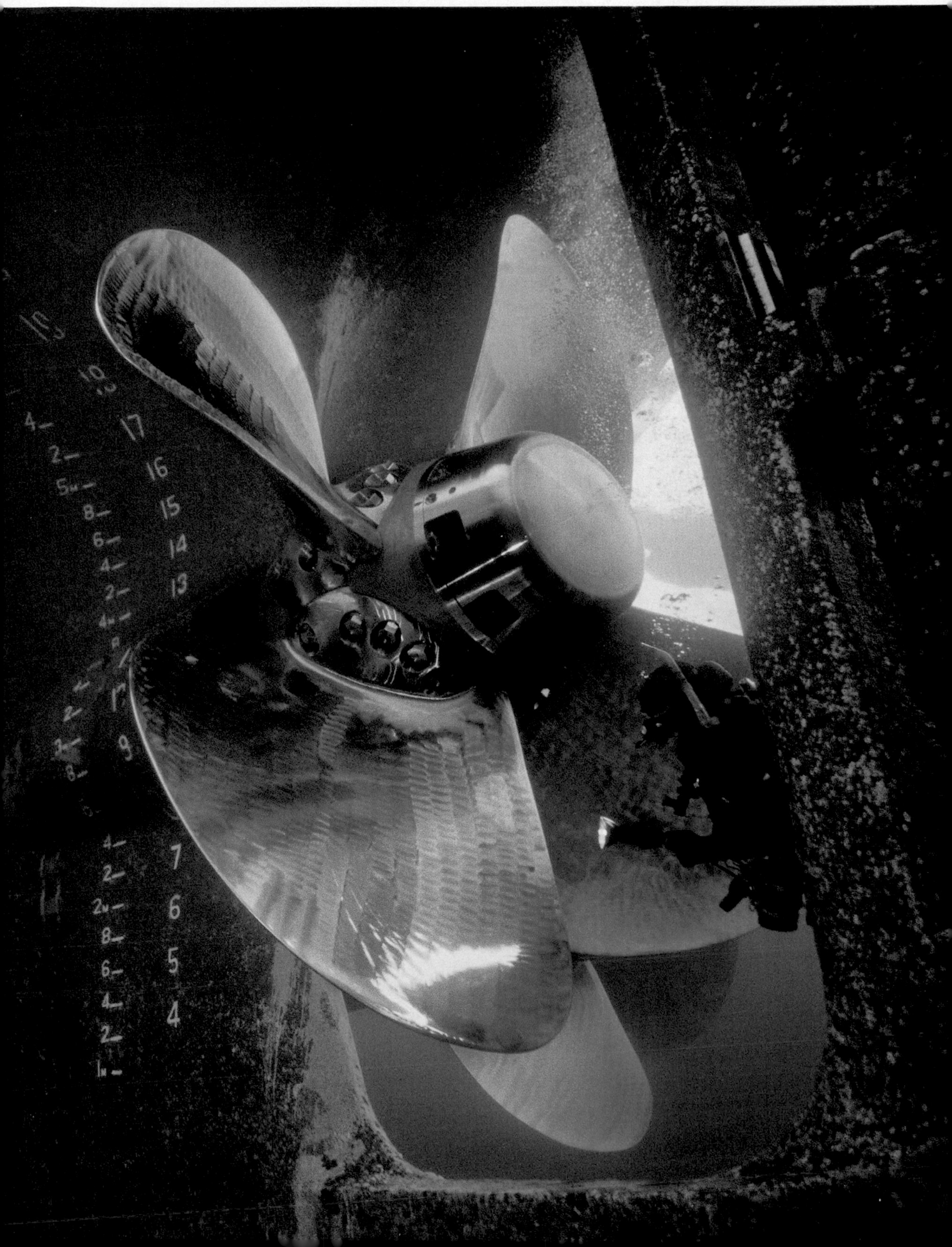

Weslaco, Texas Ruffled, tiaraed, and manicured, twins Vanessa and Veronica Del Toro wait to leave for their *quinceañera* reception—the 15th-birthday party that, in Latino culture, marks their coming of age.

See more Visions of Earth images at **visionsofearth.ngm.com.**

PHOTO: PENNY DE LOS SANTOS

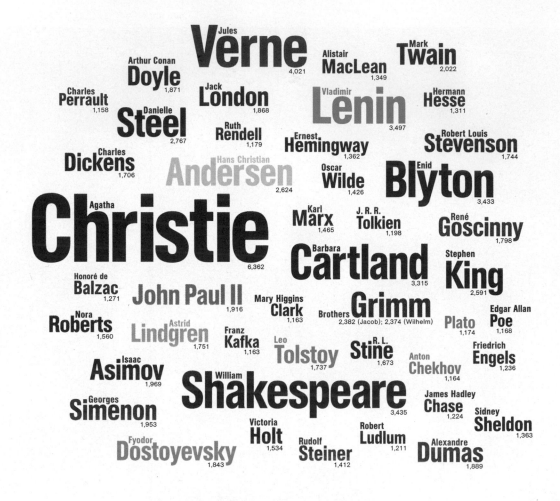

Jules Verne 4,021
Alistair MacLean 1,349
Mark Twain 2,022
Arthur Conan Doyle 1,871
Charles Perrault 1,158
Jack London 1,868
Vladimir Lenin 3,497
Hermann Hesse 1,311
Danielle Steel 2,767
Ruth Rendell 1,179
Ernest Hemingway 1,362
Robert Louis Stevenson 1,744
Charles Dickens 1,706
Hans Christian Andersen 2,624
Oscar Wilde 1,426
Enid Blyton 3,433
Agatha Christie 6,362
Karl Marx 1,465
J. R. R. Tolkien 1,198
René Goscinny 1,798
Honoré de Balzac 1,271
John Paul II 1,916
Barbara Cartland 3,315
Stephen King 2,591
Nora Roberts 1,560
Astrid Lindgren 1,751
Mary Higgins Clark 1,163
Brothers Grimm 2,382 (Jacob); 2,374 (Wilhelm)
Plato 1,174
Edgar Allan Poe 1,168
Isaac Asimov 1,969
Franz Kafka 1,163
Leo Tolstoy 1,737
R. L. Stine 1,673
Anton Chekhov 1,164
Friedrich Engels 1,236
Georges Simenon 1,953
William Shakespeare 3,435
James Hadley Chase 1,224
Sidney Sheldon 1,363
Fyodor Dostoyevsky 1,843
Victoria Holt 1,534
Rudolf Steiner 1,412
Robert Ludlum 1,211
Alexandre Dumas 1,889

Most in Translation

In this UNESCO compilation of most translated authors, size of
last name corresponds to number of translations (listed below name).
Color indicates language of original publication.

- ■ English
- ■ German
- ■ French
- ■ Russian
- ■ Danish
- ■ Ancient Greek
- ■ Italian/Latin/Polish
- ■ Swedish

UNESCO's Index Translationum speaks volumes about topics
and authors of global appeal. The bibliography of translations
lists some 1.7 million books from 130 countries in 820 languages.
Along with the authors above, works by Walt Disney Productions
and the Old and New Testament are among the most widely translated. J. K. Rowling hasn't cracked the top 50—yet. But lots of U.S.
authors have. "Translation from other languages into American
English," says Rainer Schulte, of the Center for Translation Studies
at the University of Texas, Dallas, "is limited in comparison to what
gets translated from English into other languages." —*Diane Cole*

GRAPHIC: OLIVER UBERTI, NG STAFF. PHOTO: REBECCA HALE, NG STAFF.

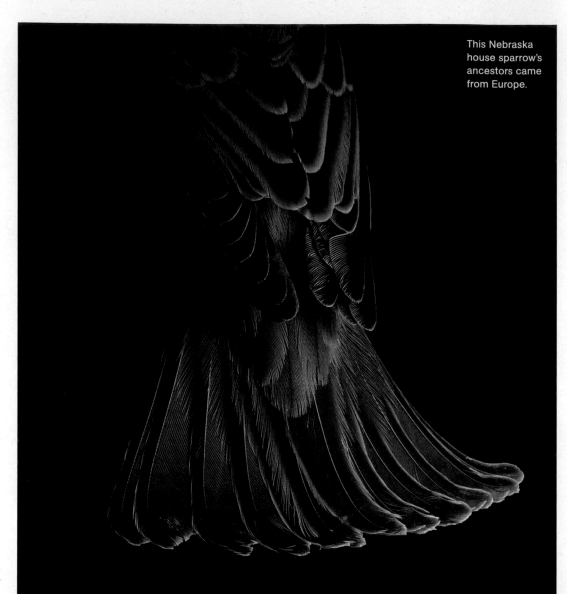

This Nebraska house sparrow's ancestors came from Europe.

Sparrow Dive House sparrows—native to Europe, Asia, and North Africa— are bound to humans. They eat our urban crumbs, nest under our eaves, and have followed us across the globe. But now their numbers are dropping—maybe because of us. In western Europe, changes in agricultural practices a few decades ago meant fewer stray seeds and weeds, and a decline in rural sparrows. Then some city populations started falling. In London, where the Royal Society for the Protection of Birds and many bird enthusiasts have studied the issue intensely, a 1925 survey counted 2,603 house sparrows in the city's Kensington Gardens; a follow-up in 2000 found only 8. A recent Royal Society study says sparrows aren't catching enough insects to feed their summer hatchlings. Some conservationists wonder if more pavement and less greenery are the culprits. —*Helen Fields*

The fastest, most reliable mobile broadband in the galaxy.

Leap into hyperdrive. With Vodafone's mobile broadband you get download speeds of up to 7.2Mbps on your laptop, which is as quick as most home broadband. It's also super reliable. Simply plug in the compact USB stick modem and get online straight away. Call 08080 000 039 today to enjoy mobile broadband that's light years ahead.

Experience in store today

Make the most of now

you can
Canon

LET'S PLAY

EOS 450D

Be creative. Get out there. Play. Get your hands on the new EOS 450D with 12.2 Megapixel sensor, 3.5 fps continuous shooting and 3.0" LCD with Live View mode. Start exploring at **www.canon.co.uk/LETSPLAY**

EURO 2008
Austria-Switzerland

ENVIRONMENT

Dead in the Water

It forms each spring and hits its lethal peak in summer—a blighted, oxygen-starved patch of the Gulf of Mexico. "Dead zones" occur around the world, from the Chesapeake Bay to the Baltic Sea. The biggest culprit? Agricultural runoff. In this case, fertilizer from upstream fields runs down the Mississippi River to the Gulf, where it spurs algae blooms. When the algae die (or are eaten and egested by zooplankton), they decompose on the bottom, depleting the oxygen, suffocating sea life—and hurting livelihoods. Clint Guidry, a Louisiana shrimper, says, "People can't imagine how much marine life this is killing." Last year's dead zone was the third largest since monitoring began in the 1980s, but 2008's could top it: The push for ethanol fuel means farmers are planting more corn, a crop often heavily fertilized. —*Chris Carroll*

Dead Zone, 2007

Mississippi River Basin

HOW THE DEAD ZONE KILLS

1 Fertilizer and other compounds empty from the Mississippi River into Gulf waters.

2 In spring, freshwater runoff creates a barrier layer, cutting off the salt water below from the oxygen in the air.

3 Problem: Various fertilizers and the warming waters cause an algae bloom.

4 Dead algae sink to the bottom and are decomposed by bacteria, depleting the oxygen in deep water.

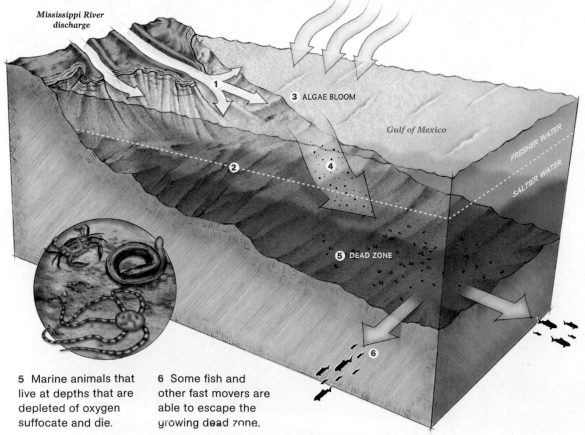

5 Marine animals that live at depths that are depleted of oxygen suffocate and die.

6 Some fish and other fast movers are able to escape the growing dead zone.

ART: HIRAM HENRIQUEZ, NG STAFF
SOURCES: NANCY N. RABALAIS, LOUISIANA UNIVERSITIES MARINE CONSORTIUM;
JAMES M. COLEMAN, COASTAL STUDIES INSTITUTE, LOUISIANA STATE UNIVERSITY. NGM MAPS

NORWAY

The first time you see the fjords is a moment you will never forget.

Photo: Terje Rakke

Let us take you on a journey of the senses. Crystal clear fjords, majestic mountains, uncrowded countryside and white sandy beaches – and it's a lot closer than you think. You'll discover breathtaking scenery, fresh mountain air and a vibrant culture, all designed to make you feel alive. Whether you take a coastal cruise or a short break, you'll never be far from nature at its most magnificent and unspoilt. See, hear, smell, taste, touch Norway.

For your free Visit Norway pack
visitnorway.co.uk or call
01443 828 818 quoting TR01

HEALTH

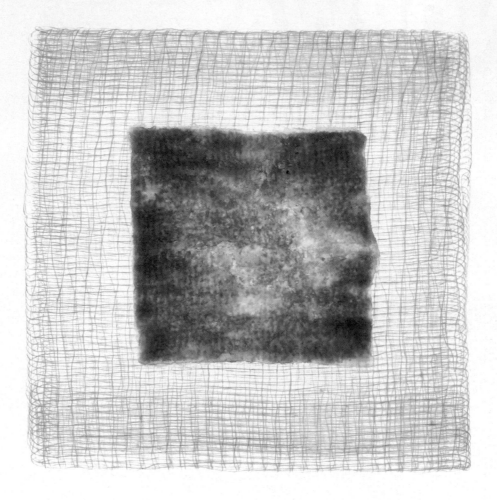

Wound and burn centers in many countries use the two-inch-square manuka honey bandage, here backed by gauze.

Sweet Fix As bacteria grow increasingly resistant to antibiotics, doctors around the world are rediscovering an old ally: honey. A popular medicine before the era of modern wonder drugs, honey fights bacteria in wounds in several ways, including the steady production of hydrogen peroxide, an antiseptic. For several years hospitals in Asia and Europe have been using bandages infused with an unusually potent honey from the manuka trees of New Zealand, and now U.S. and Canadian institutions are following their lead. The antiseptic strength of each batch's magic bullet—called the Unique Manuka Factor—is rated from zero to 25. Scientists still haven't fully identified which of more than a hundred possible substances packs the powerhouse punch, but its presence means there's a good chance the honey will stick as a treatment —A. R. Williams

ROB'S NATURE VALLEY

Symonds Yat, Forest of Dean

This view's still as beautiful as the first time I saw it.

Nature Valley Oats'n Honey Crunchy Granola bars, made with natural wholegrain oats, and delicious pure honey. Let them take you wherever you want to go.

Where's your Nature Valley?

For over 1000 walks visit www.naturevalley.co.uk
Find us in the biscuit aisle

Similar in size to a chimpanzee, a bonobo stretches out in the canopy to eat.

NG GRANT A Boon for Bonobos In the great ape family, bonobos are the cheeky, easy-going members. Not for them aggressive, chest-pounding displays of dominance. They are lovers, seldom fighters. In their female-dominated societies, individuals copulate to settle conflicts. Bonobos also engage in communal sex to ease strains at a new feeding site.

To help save this singular and endangered primate, found only in the rain forests of the Democratic Republic of the Congo, the DRC government and U.S.-based Bonobo Conservation Initiative have created a vast sanctuary. Larger than the state of Massachusetts, the 11,803-square-mile Sankuru Nature Reserve likely harbors several thousand bonobos out of an estimated population of 50,000. (Numbers are inexact, as a decade of civil war has kept researchers out of the area.) To make the reserve work, local communities have vowed to stop killing bonobos for meat, the chief threat, in return for development aid. Sankuru is the first part in a network of planned reserves to be called the Bonobo Peace Forest. —*Tom O'Neill*

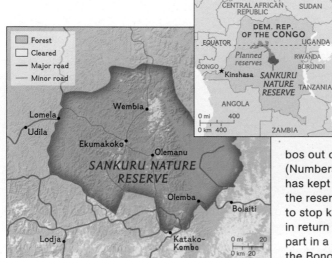

PHOTO: TAKESHI FURUICHI, KYOTO UNIVERSITY. NGM MAPS. SOURCE: BONOBO CONSERVATION INITIATIVE

more is
always
on the way

Turkey
welcomes you

Turkish Culture and Tourism Office
Tel: +44 (0) 20 7839 7778 • www.gototurkey.co.uk

TURKISH AIRLINES
www.thy.com

GEOGRAPHY

Last Colonies
In 2002 East Timor won full independence from Indonesia. Since then no territory anywhere has achieved self-government. Nearly 50 years after the UN said colonialism must end, that organization lists 16 places, and 1.2 million people, still under foreign rule. Two colonial powers, the U.S. and the U.K., refuse to cooperate with the UN. France will let New Caledonia vote next decade on its future. And New Zealand urged Tokelau to choose equal partnership, but a 2007 referendum failed—by 16 votes. —*Karen E. Lange*

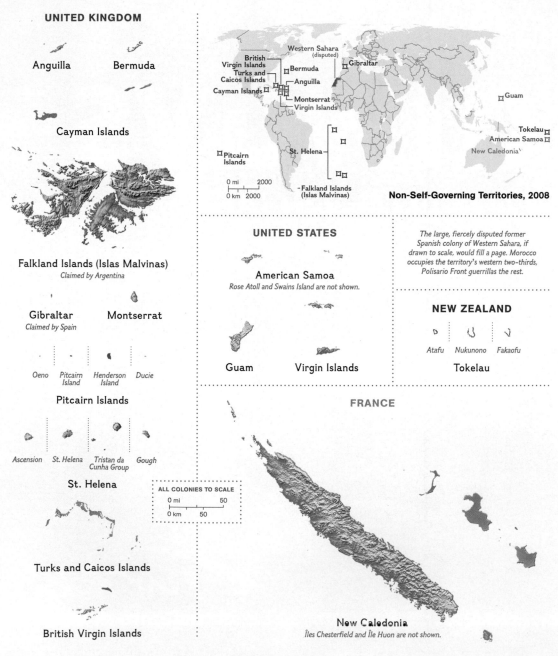

UNITED KINGDOM

Anguilla

Bermuda

Cayman Islands

Falkland Islands (Islas Malvinas)
Claimed by Argentina

Gibraltar
Claimed by Spain

Montserrat

Oeno · Pitcairn Island · Henderson Island · Ducie

Pitcairn Islands

Ascension · St. Helena · Tristan da Cunha Group · Gough

St. Helena

Turks and Caicos Islands

British Virgin Islands

Non-Self-Governing Territories, 2008

Western Sahara (disputed)
British Virgin Islands
Turks and Caicos Islands
Cayman Islands
Bermuda
Anguilla
Montserrat
Virgin Islands
Gibraltar
Guam
Tokelau
American Samoa
New Caledonia
Pitcairn Islands
St. Helena
Falkland Islands (Islas Malvinas)

0 mi 2000
0 km 2000

UNITED STATES

American Samoa
Rose Atoll and Swains Island are not shown.

Guam

Virgin Islands

The large, fiercely disputed former Spanish colony of Western Sahara, if drawn to scale, would fill a page. Morocco occupies the territory's western two-thirds, Polisario Front guerrillas the rest.

NEW ZEALAND

Atafu · Nukunono · Fakaofu

Tokelau

ALL COLONIES TO SCALE
0 mi 50
0 km 50

FRANCE

New Caledonia
Îles Chesterfield and Île Huon are not shown.

↖ **Learn more** about the world's last colonies at **ngm.com**.

NGM MAPS. SOURCE: UNITED NATIONS

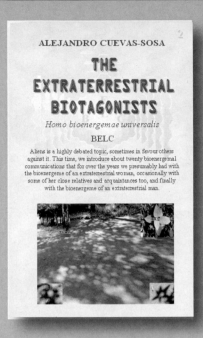

If the Stones Could Speak

SEARCHING FOR THE MEANING OF STONEHENGE

BY CAROLINE ALEXANDER NATIONAL GEOGRAPHIC CONTRIBUTING WRITER

PHOTOGRAPHS BY KEN GEIGER NATIONAL GEOGRAPHIC STAFF

Long studied yet enigmatic still, the monument looms over England's Salisbury Plain.

KINDRED SITES

At twilight on Salisbury Plain in 1500 B.C., a falcon's-eye view takes in a land tattooed with earthworks, most by that time abandoned. Durrington Walls (foreground), a henge nearly two miles northeast of Stonehenge and 20 times larger, once held circular timber monuments, as did adjacent Woodhenge. Cryptic trenches like the Cursus are numerous in Britain. Avenues from Stonehenge and Durrington Walls to the River Avon suggest to some scholars that the sites were ritually linked.

Avenue

River Avon

ART BY KAZUHIKO SANO

Stonehenge

Cursus

Burial mounds

Woodhenge

Durrington Walls
Southern Circle
Northern Circle

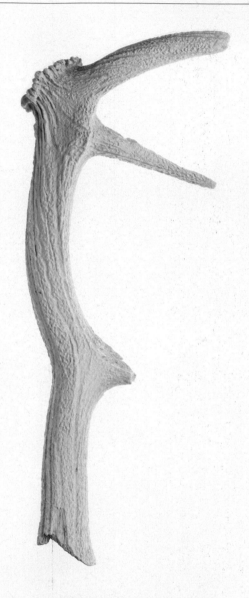

Their tips blunted as Neolithic laborers used them
to gouge through chalky ground, antler picks carved
massive earthworks at Stonehenge and Durrington
Walls. The picks give archaeologists a means of carbon
dating the sites where they're found.

The earliest metal knives found in Britain come from
the grave of a rich man buried a few miles from Stonehenge
around 2400 B.C. Made of soft copper from France and
Spain, they were likely duller than the flint knives typical of
the age, and may have been used only for ceremony.

HEARTH AND HOME

Who used Stonehenge? Clues are being found in a recently unearthed Neolithic village at Durrington Walls—the largest known in Britain—tentatively dated at between 2600 and 2500 B.C. Archaeologist Mike Parker Pearson believes the perhaps 300 wattle-and-daub houses, with wooden beds and hearth-warmed plaster floors, were seasonally occupied when people gathered for the winter and summer solstices.

ART BY KAZUHIKO SANO

(Continued from page 38) straddle a hundred-foot-wide flint-paved avenue to the Avon. Standing inside the foundation outline of one of the houses, Mike Parker Pearson pointed out domestic details, such as an oval hearth in the middle of the floor. "These are heel, or maybe buttock, marks," he said, squatting by way of demonstration beside indentations on the plaster floor. Remains of a cooking area stood to one side. Five houses show evidence of furniture, including slot marks for the edges of wooden beds. Parker Pearson waved a hand toward the dark tree fringe in the distance. Trial excavations and geophysical surveys have detected a multitude of other possible hearths in the valley. "There may be as many as 300 houses," he said, making it the largest Neolithic settlement found in Britain.

Drawing on field experience in Madagascar, Parker Pearson advocates a bold interpretation of the site and, with it, the "answer" to Stonehenge. In Malagasy culture, the ancestors are revered with stone monuments, signifying the hardening of bodies to bone and the enduring commemoration of death; wood, by contrast, which decays, is associated with transient life. Stone is ancestral and male, while wood, as Parker Pearson put it, is "soft and squishy, like women and babies." As he allows, no such gender distinction has yet been discerned in Britain, but it's the same principle underlying Western commemorative practice: "You lay flowers on the grave, then you put up a tombstone."

Guided by this model, Parker Pearson sees suggestive associations between Durrington Walls, with its defining wooden structures, and the hard monumentality of Stonehenge. Durrington has a path to the Avon that could be a ceremonial avenue, though it is just over 550 feet long, while that at Stonehenge runs a mile and three-quarters, and its processional character is defined by flanking ditches and banks.

To Parker Pearson, the contrasts are equally suggestive. Stonehenge is aligned on both the

Sifting rubble from the Cursus—a Neolithic earthwork half a mile from Stonehenge—archaeology students look for small artifacts. Last year some 270 people worked on the Stonehenge Riverside Project, a major dig examining multiple sites in Salisbury Plain's ancient ceremonial landscape. The aim: to discover if the plain's monuments had interlocking purposes.

axis of the summer solstice sunrise and the winter solstice sunset, while the Southern Circle at Durrington Walls catches the winter solstice sunrise. A profusion of pottery and animal bone debris, especially of pigs, implies that Durrington Walls saw much feasting, while very little pottery has been found at Stonehenge. Scarcely any human remains have been found at Durrington, but 52 cremations and many other burials have been uncovered at Stonehenge, which may contain as many as 240—the largest Neolithic cemetery in England. Durrington, in this new theory, represents the domain of the living, and Stonehenge, the domain of the ancestral dead, with the two linked by seasonal processions along

■ **Society Grant** This research is funded in part by your Society membership.

a route formed by the avenues and the river. The ashes of most of the dead would have been entrusted to the river. Other cremated remains, possibly the society's elite, were deposited ceremonially at Stonehenge itself.

"Many specialists would go along with the dead and living in a loose sort of way," said Mike Pitts, editor of the journal *British Archaeology* and one of the few people around today who have actually excavated at Stonehenge. It is the details of the new theory that are problematic. The assumption has always been that burial remains at Stonehenge were common only during the period of the pre-stone earthworks and timber structures, though Parker Pearson

now believes they continued into the period of the stones. But environmental evidence from the immediate landscape around Stonehenge indicates the usual activities of the living, such as farming and grazing of animals, which do not seem compatible with a larger ritualized domain of the dead. And there is no agreement about when the sarsen stones arrived. Similarly, the date of the avenue leading from Stonehenge to the Avon, the necessary link between the two sites, needs to be resolved by more evidence. Filling in these gaps is crucial for any meaningful correlation of activities between the two sites.

Summing up, Pitts said of Parker Pearson's theory: "The value of this interpretation is not

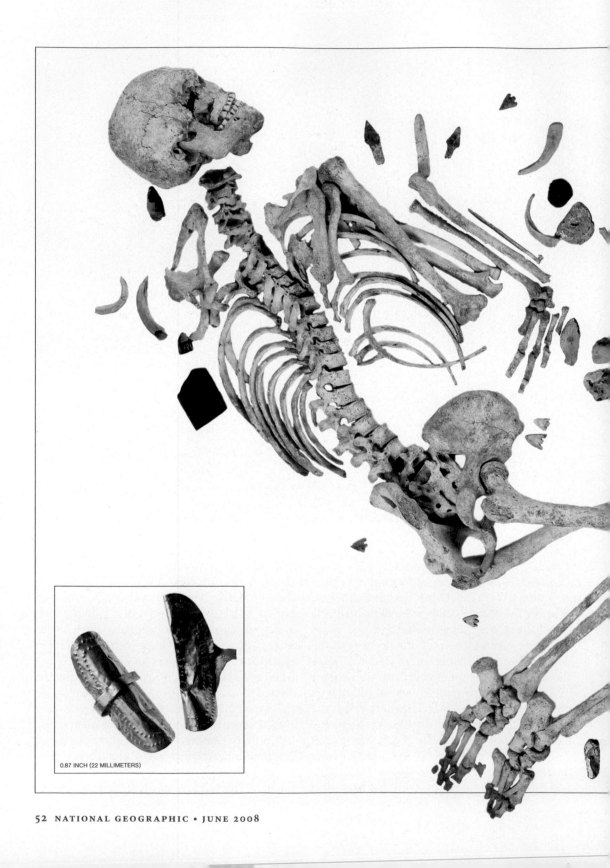

0.87 INCH (22 MILLIMETERS)

DISTANT TRAVELER

The man was footloose and fabulously rich. Isotopic tooth analysis shows that the "Amesbury Archer," unearthed in 2002, grew up in the Alps. He was buried around 2400 B.C. with metalworking tools, a quiver of fine arrows, and the earliest gold yet found in Britain—hair ornaments (lower left). What brought him to within a few miles of Stonehenge at its height? Another mystery.

just the idea of linking stones and ancestors, but that it works with the entire landscape. Previous interpretations have taken the independent sites separately."

IRONICALLY, A MORE DIRECT approach to the heart of Stonehenge might lie in fieldwork far from its own landscape, miles away in a small site amid convulsed, fractured outcrops of dolerite and shale in the Preseli Mountains of southwestern Wales—the source of Stonehenge's oldest stones, the fabled bluestones. The erection of the bluestones marked a critical transition from the original timber settings toward the monument we have today. "Dusted with magic," is how one archaeologist described the famously atmospheric hills to me, in a region long known for its intriguing stone circles, dolmens, and other megalithic monuments. As long ago as 1923, specific outcrops around Carn Menyn, at the eastern end of the Preseli hills, had been identified as the bluestone source; subsequent geochemical work in 1991 refined this to roughly one square mile.

Yet for more than 80 years after the discovery of the bluestone source, "no one actually got their trowel out and did anything," said Timothy Darvill, a professor of archaeology at Bournemouth University. "It's perverse, really." Together with Geoffrey Wainwright, a distinguished authority on the Neolithic and the original excavator of Durrington Walls in the 1960s, Darvill began a systematic survey around Carn Menyn in 2001, accompanied by a small team of researchers from Bournemouth University, including Yvette Staelens, a senior lecturer. "It's a place where strange things happen," Staelens said of the hills. She described reaching the top of a sheer rock outcrop and finding a fox impaled on rock. "Guts and blood were spilling down— we think a large raptor must have dropped it. Strange things like that."

"It's a natural monument," said Wainwright, of the chaotic rock formations of columns and pillars that litter the ground. "The stones of Stonehenge didn't have to be quarried; they could be simply carried off." Up to six feet in

Nature alone set up these standing stones in Wales's Preseli Mountains, source of the first stones installed at Stonehenge—the bluestones. Local folklore attributes healing power to springs gushing from the hills, and some researchers speculate that's why the stones were moved 250 miles east. Stonehenge may have been a place of healing.

ANDREW HENDERSON

54

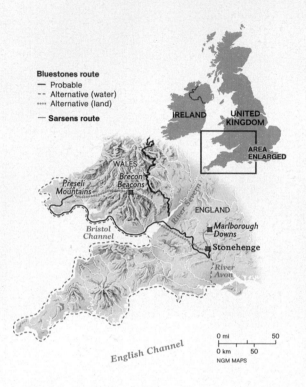

Microscopic analysis (below) of Stonehenge's bluestones confirms their Welsh origin in hilly terrain. Their quarrying and transport along a land and water route of 250 miles (map, left) required coordination among several populations. But more than a thousand years earlier, people in the Preseli Mountains were already moving stones, building tombs like one at Pentre Ifan (right), foreshadowing what was to come.

height and four tons, the approximately 80 original bluestones—the exact number formerly located at Stonehenge is unclear—are mostly dolerite spotted with milky feldspar. Freshly cut and wet with rain, they do indeed glisten blue. Still, these are not the only striking stones within the British Isles. "Why did they bring these stones 250 miles to build Stonehenge?" Wainwright asked. "And why did they retain these stones throughout its structural history?"

So far the Preseli hills have not yielded an answer, but they do offer some clues. As Staelens recalled, on the first day Wainwright and Darvill began their field survey, Wainwright laid his hand on a rock. "And it had rock art. The pair of them were very academic blokey about the discovery. Geoff said, 'Look at this, Tim.' Tim said, 'That looks important, Geoff.' They just stood there, very British low-key."

The handful of examples they eventually discovered of the distinctive "cup mark" art, a motif of circular hollows within hollows, could

be dated only very broadly at between 3800 and 2000 B.C. "We didn't get anything we could confidently put in for dating," Darvill said. This much, however, is known: Perhaps as early as 4000 B.C., people were constructing monuments in this atmospheric area where rock pinnacles seem to pierce the sky and commemorating the site with motifs associated elsewhere with "special" sites. "In Neolithic times people are going to the Preseli hills and venerating them," was how one archaeologist put it.

Whether the stones were moved to Salisbury Plain in a single, sustained campaign or an ongoing effort spread out over a generation or more is not known. Similarly, how the stones were transported has been hotly debated over the years. "That's a blue-collar question," Wainwright said, relishing what was clearly a well-rehearsed line, "and I am not an engineer." Although glacial drift may initially have worked the stones loose from the hills, an old theory that glaciers swept them onto Salisbury Plain has been

discounted by modern studies; somehow people must have moved them. The shortest accepted route—by river and along the coast of Wales, across the Severn estuary, into the upper reaches of the Avon—is about 250 miles. It is impossible to judge just how remarkable a feat such transport was in its day. As Darvill points out, in continental Europe even more massive stones were being lugged around. "Increasingly, the 'unaccountable effort' argument is under attack," Darvill said. "The Grand Menhir in Brittany—what does it weigh? Three hundred and forty tons, something like that, and it was moved at least a few miles." Whether the stones were pulled by teams of men or oxen, on sleds with greased tracks, giant rollers of wood, or some other unsuspected means, Neolithic man evidently, as Darvill said, "had transportation sorted out."

Archaeologists can only speculate about the significance of the bluestones. Carn Menyn may have been a landmark charged with special meaning in a key overland route for trade or travel. Some claim the arrangement of the types of bluestone—dolerite, rhyolite, and tuff—at Stonehenge mirrors their natural arrangement on Carn Menyn. Then again, perhaps the very effort of transporting the stones or their exotic nature was the point—a kind of statement of ability and power.

Darvill and Wainwright believe the answer lies in an old tradition. Writing in the 12th century A.D., Geoffrey of Monmouth, in his rambling, gossipy meander through the history of the kings of Britain, gave a fanciful account of how Stonehenge was carried bodily—on the orders of the wizard Merlin, no less—from Ireland to Salisbury Plain, where it was set down to be a place of healing. The story may represent oddments of tenaciously preserved folk memory garbled by a long—in this case, 3,600-year-old—oral tradition; the stones of Stonehenge were, after all, brought from a far place in the west by seemingly magical means.

Rounding out this story is an old local belief,

still potent today, that attributes healing powers to springs arising in the Preseli hills. The sum of these two traditions posits Stonehenge as a kind of Lourdes of the prehistoric world. Among colleagues this healing theory has received a mixed, but cautiously interested, reception. "I mean, it's plausible," one expert said. Until further evidence comes to light, then, the trail returns to where it began, with only the most basic of hard facts: People had found something special in the Preseli hills and transported this to southern England.

AT THE TIME the bluestones arrived on what is now Salisbury Plain, the old-growth forest had been cleared for centuries into open grassland. If brought by river, the stones would have been dragged from the willow-and-sedge-lined banks of the Avon up to the site. Decoratively stippled, grooved and smoothed, the stones were erected in pairs to form a double arc and were perhaps also yoked by lintels that have since fallen away.

The old earthworks were now refashioned to highlight the northeast entrance, thus confirming the import of the monument's alignment with the solstices—an emphasis that perhaps reflected beliefs about the meaning of the stones in their location at Preseli, or perhaps the new beliefs of a changing age. At some later date the giant sarsens of hard sandstone were dragged in from the Marlborough Downs, 20 to 30 miles away. Although subsequent ages would fiddle with the internal design, the erection of the sarsens—the great broad-shouldered guardians of the smaller stones from Wales—bestowed on Stonehenge its enduring aura of unassailable assurance. Mystifying as it is to us, there is no mistaking the confident purposefulness of its massive, monumental features.

Studies conducted by Michael Allen, an expert in environmental archaeology, demonstrate that throughout the long period of Stonehenge's construction, people of the area carried on with the mundane tasks of their lives. Charcoal remains, pollens of weeds associated with crops, and, most valuably, snail shells—which can be matched to different habitats—show that the Stonehenge landscape was cleared, grazed, and farmed. Whatever its function, Stonehenge was embedded in the community it served. "I see it being used like a cathedral, or Wembley Stadium," Allen said. "Some days it was used to hold solemn rituals, other days for more ordinary gatherings."

That so much has been found so recently on this historic landscape underscores how much may yet be revealed. Projected work on the avenue could establish when it was extended to the Avon, clarifying at what stage the river became ritually linked to the monument. Cremation remains that were excavated and reburied at the monument as long ago as 1935 could benefit from rigorous new analysis with up-to-date technology. In April Timothy Darvill and Geoffrey Wainwright conducted a two-week dig inside the stone circle—the first such excavation in decades—hoping to pin down when the bluestones arrived. Their planned reexamination of skeletal remains from the Stonehenge region may indicate whether a high percentage of the people had been in need of "healing." Fieldwork already under way in the Preseli hills may yield datable burial finds, possibly shedding light on the significance of the Preseli stones.

TO ALL THOSE who seek to read the meaning of Stonehenge in its stones, ritual texts from the dawn of history offer cautionary tales. Take, for example, a random Late Bronze Age text of ritual practice from the Luwians, who lived in what is now Turkey between roughly 1700 B.C. and 800 B.C.: "Then they hold it [the sheep] out to him and he spits into its mouth twice. The Old Woman speaks as follows, 'Spit out pain and woe, the god's anger....' Then they bring a piglet of dough and a living piglet. They wave the living piglet at some distance." It is fair to say that no diligent fieldwork or application of logic and reason could have led even a visionary archaeologist to reconstruct this ritual from artifacts like bones and ceramics. There are no texts to explain Stonehenge. Secure in its wordless prehistory, it can thus absorb a multitude of "meanings": temple to the sun—or the moon,

Weathered and broken, but still guarding secrets after more than 4,500 years, Stonehenge is the heart of an elaborately sculpted landscape. This spring, archaeologists excavated within the circle, hoping to determine when the first stones arrived—and solve a piece of the puzzle.

for that matter; astronomical calendar; city of the ancestral dead; center of healing; stone representation of the gods; symbol of status and power. The heart of its mystique is, surely, that it excites in equal measure both zealous certitude and utter bafflement.

Stonehenge represented the end of the grand tradition of monument building in Neolithic England. It fell out of use around 1500 B.C., and over the centuries many of its stones toppled, broke, or were carried off—casualties of nature as well as man. From time to time reports were made about the enigmatic ruins. A first-century B.C. Greek historian, Diodorus of Sicily, cites a lost account set down three centuries earlier, which described "a magnificent precinct sacred to Apollo and a notable spherical temple" on a large island in the far north, opposite what is now France. (Apollo, intriguingly, is the god of healing.)

In more recent history Samuel Pepys, the great diarist, visited the stones in the summer of 1668, hiring horses and a guide to take him over the plain. His account still resonates today. The stones, he wrote, were "as prodigious as any tales I ever heard of them and worth going this journey to see. God knows what their use was." ☐

➤ **Enter the Henge** Explore Stonehenge in a 3-D photographic model at **ngm.com**.

send me to

Brightening the long Siberian winter, ice sculptures gleam in
Khanty-Mansiysk, resurgent capital of Russia's richest oil region.

Siberia
Oil transforms a Russian outpost

NEW PERKS at the Rodnichok —"little spring"—kindergarten in Surgut include a heated pool. The 30-year-old school, now city owned, has been transformed with funds flowing into public coffers from the region's thriving energy operations.

MUD-SPATTERED and cold, oil workers change a drilling pipe. Russia's oil industry has been expanding for nearly a decade, its growth fueled by surging world oil prices. National production has reached nearly ten million barrels a day.

GAS FLARES and rig lights sear
the night sky in the Savuiskoye
oil field. Russia is now the
world's top producer of crude
oil. Some 70 percent of its
reserves are found in western
Siberia. Once extracted, most oil
is shipped to foreign consumers.

BY PAUL STAROBIN

PHOTOGRAPHS BY GERD LUDWIG

It's around midnight,

and the couples on the dance floor at the Palace Restaurant are gently swaying to a slow one. *"Za nas, za neft*—To us, to oil," the singer croons,

> *Wherever life sends us,*
> *To us, to oil…*
> *We fill our glasses to the brim.*

It is Oilers' Day in the western Siberian province of Khanty-Mansi. This annual holiday, honoring the hard labor of the oil workers, the *neftyaniki,* falls early in September, after the worst of the summer mosquito season and before the first snowfall, in October. Hours earlier, as daylight faded, thousands crowded into a huge outdoor sports complex. A stage was framed by a deep-green backdrop of unbroken forest. Balloons were released, torches were lit, and a troupe belted out a song:

> *There is only one joy for us,*
> *And this is all we need,*
> *To wash our faces in the new oil,*
> *Of the drilling rig.*

Little wonder Russians are toasting oil: These are boom times. Global oil prices have increased tenfold since 1998, and Russia has pulled ahead of Saudi Arabia as the world's top crude oil producer. The Kremlin's budget now overflows with funds for new schools, roads, and national defense projects, and Moscow's nouveau riche are plunking down millions of dollars for mansion-scale "dachas."

The pumping heart of the boom is western Siberia's boggy oil fields, which produce around 70 percent of Russia's oil—some seven million barrels a day. For Khanty-Mansi, a territory nearly the size of France, the bonanza provides an unparalleled opportunity to create modern, even desirable living conditions in a region

whose very name evokes a harsh, desolate place. Khanty-Mansi's regional capital, scene of the holiday revelries, is being rebuilt with oil-tax proceeds. The new structures include an airport terminal (once a wooden shack with an outhouse), an art museum featuring paintings by 19th-century Russian masters, and a pair of lavishly equipped boarding schools for children gifted in mathematics and the arts. Even the provincial town of Surgut, a backwater only a few decades ago, is laying out new suburbs and is plagued by traffic jams.

But the opportunity presented by oil could slip through the region's fingers. Despite the remarkable surge in oil prices, oil production in western Siberia has leveled off in recent years. Output barely rose from 2004 to 2007—a period when the rulers of the Kremlin, a cold-eyed and control-oriented crew, seized choice fields once held by private oil barons. The oligarchs, as they were known, were rapacious sorts who jousted among themselves for spoils. But they also heavily invested in the fields in order to maximize production and profits. The Kremlin, by contrast, aims to exploit oil not only as a source of national wealth, but also as a political tool for making Russia a great world power once again. Its heavy-handed tactics have made foreign investors wary and could undermine the boom—and with it Khanty-Mansi's chances for a brighter future.

WESTERN SIBERIA'S great oil deposits lie under lands that an exiled Marxist revolutionary, suffering in the gulag, once called the "waste places of the Earth." But to someone visiting by choice, oil country looks fetchingly wild and pristine. The terrain is dominated by taiga—dense forest of spindly birch, cedar, and pine—and *boloto,*

...rks a reception. The longtime ...its benefit his remote region.

peaty
and
no m
merc

Oi
the n
that
tappe
milita
dozer
it tur
anyon
rels ha

In t
says K
penko
years,
and a
of fros
in the

Yet despite the hardships, the ...ck at that time the way an old ...his first love for a beautiful ...ally passionate about his lat-...edevelopment of the provin-...y-Mansiysk, a town of 60,000. ...y detail, and he has the funds ...ital to his liking. The prov-...generates 40 billion dollars in s, 4.5 billion dollars of which ...to keep for its own use. The ...w.

...ground notwithstanding, ...is a distinctly non-Soviet ...leading architectural sym-...pping emporium topped by ...n dome in the shape of a ...al tent used by the region's

over the Ob River, which in the late 19th cen-tury was a route for squalid barges transporting prisoners to their final places of banishment. The bridge project took four years of toil under

Paul Starobin, former Moscow bureau chief for Business Week, *is writing a book about life after the American Century. Gerd Ludwig frequently covers Russia for* National Geographic.

TRADITIONAL LIFE for indigenous herders requires reindeer and room. Oil rigs and pipelines disrupt the nomads' access to herd migration routes and feeding grounds.

indigenous people—the Khanty, Mansi, and others who herd reindeer, hunt, and fish. That symbolism would have been unthinkable in Soviet times, when the state, with its ideological cult of "the worker," denied the very idea of culturally derived identity.

When Siberia's oil lands came under development, native people were forcibly herded into villages and cut off from their hunting and fishing grounds. Following the breakup of the Soviet Union, the nomads won legal status as "aboriginal people," with the right to roam the oil fields. In spite of their new status and the architectural homage in the capital, their lot has hardly improved. Their numbers are small, about 30,000 in all; their languages are

nearly extinct; and they are heavily afflicted by the scourges of contemporary Russia—AIDS, alcoholism, and tuberculosis. Some oil-tax money is being invested in medical ships that stop along the rivers to care for patients. But critics say these floating clinics diagnose disease, then leave patients with no means to get treatment.

Rural Russia is also being depopulated by the flight of young people to Moscow and other cities. To counter these trends, Filipenko has implemented ambitious plans to turn Khanty-Mansi into a place young people will choose to live in rather than leave. And this effort, he boasts, is working. He notes that Khanty-Mansi has the third highest birthrate among provinces in Russia, and unlike the country as a whole,

provides consulting services to oil companies, but it also takes on projects in unrelated fields such as nanotechnology.

It's the start of a "Silicon Taiga," says Alexander Sherbakov, a 60-year-old mathematician with a gray walrus mustache. As the era of easy oil comes to an end, he says, "we're going to grow our own scholars" by creating information-age jobs for the younger generation. Unlike investment in oil, investment in science, he says, can guarantee an everlasting bright future for the region's economy and its people.

That's undoubtedly an optimistic assessment. For one thing, the touted model, Silicon Valley, is located in temperate California. In Soviet times the Kremlin could simply order top scientists to move to remote research centers. In post-Soviet times Russia's top researchers can live and work wherever they choose, and most are choosing to live in prosperous cities such as Moscow and St. Petersburg.

WHILE THE OIL BOOM has yet to make Siberia a magnet for Russia's knowledge class, it is attracting many other newcomers: impoverished immigrants from beyond Russia's borders. Early one morning, in a vacant lot just off the highway to Filipenko's showcase capital, a group of about 15 shabbily dressed men ranging in age from their 20s to their 40s are waiting for offers of work, however menial. A white Nissan pulls up, and several of the men walk over to talk to the driver, who is looking for a few hands to dig potatoes. But his offering price, just under ten dollars a day, isn't enough, and he drives away without any takers.

whose population is in decline, Khanty-Mansi's has increased 18 percent since 1989, from a combination of births and immigration.

Oil composes 90 percent of the capital's economy, which is not surprising given the surge in oil prices. But it points to a problem shared by all resource-dependent economies: At some point the resource will be exhausted, and new sources of prosperity will have to be found. Recognizing the need to develop economic prospects beyond oil, Filipenko persuaded some 80 top researchers from Akademgorodok—a famed science and research town in southern Siberia created in Soviet times—to move to his regional capital to staff a new institute specializing in information technologies. The institute

These men are what Russians, borrowing a German word, call *gastarbeiters*—guest workers. They are nearly everywhere in Khanty-Mansi. Most are Muslims from Tajikistan, the former Soviet republic in Central Asia whose economy was shattered by civil war in the mid-1990s. They come here in spring and return home before winter arrives. It's not every day they find a job, but when they do they can earn about $20 lugging bags of cement for a construction crew or doing household cleaning. They wire funds back to their families, and their employers avoid paying taxes on the wages.

The men balk at my request to see their living quarters. One says he is ashamed to show me how he lives. "I don't want you to get the

The Flow of Power

Veining the landscape, pipelines snake from Russia across Europe.
Nearly a third of overall European Union crude oil imports—worth some
60 billion dollars—come from Russia. Some nations are more depen-
dent: Poland gets 95 percent of its crude from Russian sources. Russia
has flexed its energy muscle in political disputes with former Soviet
republics, shutting off supplies—or threatening to do so—during winter.

Primary Russian oil and gas pipelines to Europe
Based on estimated volume of major pipelines

Oil pipeline
pipeline

less ◄···· volume ········► *more*

Oil or gas field

Gas pipeline
pipeline

less ◄···· volume ········► *more*

Oil Imports
Estimated market value
(in billions of dollars)
of imports of Russian
crude oil for 2007

BASED ON EUROPEAN
IMPORT DATA; NOT
AVAILABLE FOR ALL
COUNTRIES

*Norwegian
Sea*

ARCTIC CIRCLE

NORWAY
$.09

FINLAND
$3.4

SWEDEN
$1.9

Primorsk-

*North
Sea*

DEN.

ESTONIA
<$1 millic

Ventspils

*Baltic
Sea*

Būtingė

LATVIA
<$1 millic

IRELAND

UNITED
KINGDOM
$3.1

Rostock

Gdańsk

LITHUANIA

RUSSIA $2.6

NETH.
$5.6

Berlin ★

BELARUS
$4.4

BELG.
$1.3

GERMANY
$11.9

Leipzig

POLAND
$5.5

LUX.

Frankfurt ●

Prague ★ $1.5

CZECH
REP.

EUROPE

FRANCE
$5.0

SWITZ.

AUSTRIA
$0.4

SLOVAKIA
$1.9

PORTUGAL
$0.4

Milan ●

SLOV.

HUNGARY
$1.6

ROMANIA
$1.6

SPAIN
$2.5

Omišalj ●

CROATIA
$1.3

BOSN.
&
HERZG.
$.05

SERBIA

ITALY
$6.3

Adriatic Sea

MONT.

BULGARIA

MACED.
$0.3

ALBAN.

Mediterranean Sea

GREECE
$1.7

AFRICA

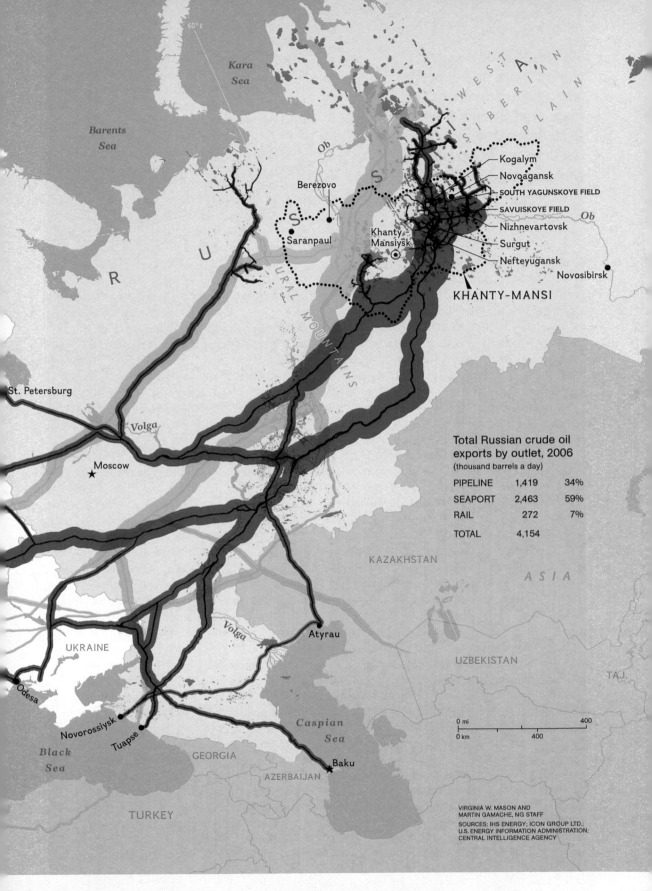

Kara
Sea

*Barents
Sea*

Berezovo

Ob

R   U   S   S
Saranpaul

Khanty-
Mansiysk ◉

60°E

W   E   S   T   E   R   N
S   I   B   E   R   I   A   N   P   L   A   I   N

Kogalym
Novoagansk
SOUTH YAGUNSKOYE FIELD
SAVUISKOYE FIELD
Ob
Nizhnevartovsk
Surgut
Nefteyugansk
Novosibirsk

KHANTY-MANSI

St. Petersburg

Volga

★ Moscow

U   R   A   L   M   O   U   N   T   A   I   N   S

**Total Russian crude oil
exports by outlet, 2006**
(thousand barrels a day)

PIPELINE	1,419	34%
SEAPORT	2,463	59%
RAIL	272	7%
TOTAL	4,154	

KAZAKHSTAN

ASIA

UKRAINE

Volga

Atyrau

UZBEKISTAN

TAJ.

Odesa

Novorossiysk

Tuapse

*Caspian
Sea*

*Black
Sea*

GEORGIA

Baku

AZERBAIJAN

TURKEY

0 mi		400
0 km		400

VIRGINIA W. MASON AND
MARTIN GAMACHE, NG STAFF
SOURCES: IHS ENERGY; ICON GROUP LTD.;
U.S. ENERGY INFORMATION ADMINISTRATION;
CENTRAL INTELLIGENCE AGENCY

The *gastarbeiters* (guest workers) are nearly everywhere in Khanty-Mansi. Most are Muslims from Tajikistan, the former Soviet republic whose economy was shattered by civil war.

wrong idea," he says. "We are not bandits; we are civilized people. We just need work."

The men are supposed to obtain registration papers certifying their place of residence, but, as they tell me, they have no authorized place to live, bunking instead in unheated garages illegally rented to them. A work boss—a kind of Mafia figure—obtains papers for them by bribing the registration office, but those documents, listing a false address, leave the gastarbeiters at the mercy of the police. When they are found out, they're sometimes forced to pay a spot "fine" (read "bribe"), and repeat offenders may face deportation. Russia's federal government recently put the burden on employers to register the workers and check their identifications, but such measures are unlikely to stem the tide so long as the oil boom continues.

A FLOOD OF RUSSIANS from economically depressed cities west of the Urals is also swelling the oil towns of western Siberia. Forty years ago Surgut was a collection of wooden hovels, in a place where temperatures can plunge to minus 60 degrees Fahrenheit and midwinter darkness lasts for all but a few hours a day. Today Surgut is one of western Siberia's largest cities, with 300,000 people. The new arrivals are voting with their feet, a sign that Russia's new market economy is actually working.

The polish and prosperity on view in Surgut were once unthinkable in Russia's hinterlands. A combined day care and preschool the city recently remodeled with 5.2 million dollars largely from oil revenue now has a heated indoor swimming pool and hydromassage whirlpool; an animal collection with rabbits, turtles, and parrots; and a room with a small wooden stage on which colorfully costumed children diligently

perform fairy tales. When weather doesn't permit outdoor exercise, the children can ride around in toy cars in a large, glass-enclosed playroom kept at a moderately chilled temperature. And then the toddlers can be soothed by a hot drink from the herbal tea bar.

I understand that the "foreigner" is being shown the finest kindergarten in town, but only so much can be faked. Stuck in Surgut's traffic jams are as many Hondas, Toyotas, and Nissans as inexpensive Russian-made Ladas. Two-car families are becoming more common with the rise in living standard.

The housing stock of a typical Russian city consists of large (and ugly) multistoried concrete apartment blocks. Surgut boasts a suburban development of single-family town houses, aimed at a new upper middle class of oil company managers, bankers, and entrepreneurs. The red-brick houses, each with its own small plot of land, are being built along a tree-lined stretch of riverfront at an average cost of $400,000. Envious townspeople coined an ironic sobriquet for the elite community: *Dolina Nischikh*, Valley of the Beggars.

Surgut might have fallen apart, as did some other Russian cities, in the chaos following the collapse of the Soviet Union. That it didn't is a testament to the rootedness and stability of its political and business leadership.

"I was born in Surgut, my children were born here, and my grandchildren were born here," Alexander Sidorov, the city's longtime mayor, proudly declares. Surgut's economic anchor, the oil company Surgutneftegas, Russia's fourth largest producer, is majority owned by local managers. And unlike most Russian oil barons, who rule their western Siberian empires from Moscow, Surgutneftegas's general director, billionaire Vladimir Bogdanov, makes his home in town. Though now a towering figure in Surgut, Bogdanov started out as a common neftyanik.

Surgutneftegas is using the oil boom to finance an ambitious modernization program. At the oil field management center, computer engineers have custom designed an enormous digital map to monitor and adjust the field's performance. The map displays real-time information sent by coded radio signal from pump stations, active wells, and pipelines. From this display, managers can tell how much electric power is being

COLD WELCOME: Despite a growing need for workers, Russia is tightening its strictures on immigration. In the regional capital of Khanty-Mansiysk, federal officers inspect laborers' documents (top). Illegal workers face arrest (above), fines, and deportation. Employers can also be penalized as much as $30,000 for each worker. But lured by the prospect of lucrative jobs in a flourishing economy, guest workers from poor ex-Soviet republics continue to pour into Siberia.

BRIGHT APARTMENTS have replaced drab relics in Nizhnevartovsk, heart of oil country, and more will be needed to accommodate an expanding population. Over the next few years the city plans to spend nearly a billion dollars on new housing.

A NEW DAY begins for Andrey Patrikeyev and wife, Irina. "We now live in nice houses, enjoy galleries," says the well-off bureaucrat. "The oil industry pushed development."

consumed, whether a well needs repairs, and whether a pipeline is leaking.

Protection of the environment, barely a concern in Soviet times, is becoming part of the new ethos. It's not that the oil industry has suddenly become softhearted toward flora and fauna. Rather, high oil prices provide an incentive to minimize waste, as do license agreements that include big fines for spills. Moreover, as Russian oil firms have become global players, they've also become more sensitive to international concerns about the environment. "Maintaining a good reputation is very important," says Alexey Knizhnikov of the World Wildlife Fund in Moscow. "Otherwise, doing business becomes difficult."

Lubov Malyshkina, director of the environmental department at Surgutneftegas, is a chemical engineer with an advanced degree in the science of corrosion protection and geoecology. She also serves as an elected official in the regional parliament. In Soviet times, she says, the oil ministry in Moscow, oblivious to local conditions, would send chemicals that proved useless to treat oil spills and other hazards. Now Malyshkina's department, drawing on a nearly 500-million-dollar budget, makes its own purchases. She shows me one: a Swedish-made Truxor vehicle with tanklike treads that break up oil-saturated peat so that spills can be cleaned up. The company is also investing five million dollars in a new plant for recycling

rest off-site for up to 30 days. Alcohol is strictly forbidden. Drink all you want during your rest, the men are told, but return sober.

Yet the jobs are a route to a prosperity unimaginable a few years ago. The least experienced workers get a monthly salary of $1,000, the most senior hands as much as $4,000. And there are bonuses for exceeding daily quotas. A thrifty neftyanik can save enough to purchase a flat in Surgut's apartment complexes—if not a town house in the Valley of the Beggars.

All of this is impressive, of course. But the larger question for Surgutneftegas, and every oil firm in Khanty-Mansi, is whether they can rise to the myriad political, economic, and technical challenges on the horizon. While most analysts expect western Siberia to remain the dominant source of Russia's oil for at least the next 20 years, the region's oil fields are aging. Coaxing additional barrels of oil from the ground is becoming more difficult and expensive, and maintaining production will require infusions of capital and expertise from sources outside Russia. But burdensome taxes—all gross revenues above $25 a barrel go to the federal government—and Kremlin-backed power plays have chilled the investment climate like a Siberian blizzard. One need only visit Nefteyugansk, a city of 114,000 on the Ob River about an hour's drive from Surgut, to see why.

A BLACK GUSHER OF TROUBLE is what the oil boom has been for Nefteyugansk, which has the look and feel of an unkempt industrial park. The central plaza is strewn with iron pipes, and down by the river a crumpled barrel of Shell oil floats next to a dilapidated dock. A few paces inside the gate of the town's cemetery lies the grave of Vladimir Petukhov, the burial ground's most famous resident. In 1996 the townspeople elected Petukhov as their mayor. Two years later, as he walked to work on a June morning, he was shot to death by a pair of gunmen. An etching on his black marble gravestone depicts him in a crewneck sweater and leather jacket.

For more than ten years oil has been at the center of a violent and chaotic power struggle in Nefteyugansk. The difficulties began in the mid-1990s, when a nouveau riche Moscow banker snagged one of Russia's prime oil producers—and the town's sole large employer—in a privatization auction. The banker, Mikhail

old tires into fibers that can be mixed into the asphalt used to pave company roads.

One aspect of the oil industry here hasn't changed: The neftyanik's job is still hazardous and grueling. At a rig about an hour's drive from Surgut, villagers gathering mushrooms are dwarfed by massive pumps, whose rhythmic motion suggests a giant bird dipping its beak to the soil. Metal stairs slick with oil lead to a platform where a drill is boring through rock with a diamond-coated bit nearly a foot in diameter. It's noisy and the air is foul, but this is a good spot to be in winter, I'm told, because the platform is bathed in steam. The men work eight-hour shifts for up to 30 straight days, sleeping on-site in trailer wagons, then

A LIGHT-UP PALM TREE lures cold-weary Russians to a Surgut travel agency selling trips to seductively warm destinations: Egypt, Spain, Turkey. Symbols of success and a heated appetite for luxury, groves of bright green palms decorate discos, casinos, and billboards across western Siberia. In Khanty-Mansiysk the swagger of youth and new money keeps the dance floor busy at Territoriya Pervykh—"champions' territory"—often until five o'clock in the morning.

Khodorkovsky, made the Nefteyugansk unit the core subsidiary in his new oil company, known as Yukos. But he antagonized the city by delaying tax payments, causing city workers to go unpaid for months. Mayor Petukhov, a former neftyanik, led public protests against the new Moscow owners, who, he said, "spit into our faces, the faces of oilers." The mayor's murder, at the age of 48, outraged the townspeople, many of whom connected the deed to his stand against Yukos. "This blood is on your hands," read anti-Yukos banners put up at city hall by Petukhov's mourners.

For five years no one was brought to justice. During this time the city was governed by a corrupt official who eventually was sent to jail for swindling oil workers out of their promised retirement homes in Russia's balmy Black Sea region. Oil prices, meanwhile, went ever higher, inflating the value of Khodorkovsky's holdings. And then the hammer came down.

In June 2003, Moscow prosecutors arrested Yukos's security chief on charges of organizing the execution of Petukhov. Four months later they arrested Khodorkovsky on charges of fraud and tax evasion. Tax authorities seized the Nefteyugansk subsidiary and handed it over to a Kremlin-controlled company called Rosneft. Khodorkovsky was convicted and carted off to jail in southeastern Siberia, where his face was slashed by an inmate. Meanwhile, the security chief was convicted in a trial heavily publicized on state television. In the latest development, prosecutors announced last February that Yukos co-owner Leonid Nevzlin also would be charged in Petukhov's murder.

Perhaps it did happen the way the government claimed, but ask folks in Nefteyugansk about the murder, and they tend to shrug and say they don't know what to believe. The coordinated elements of the Yukos affair have the whiff of a Moscow plot hatched by the KGB types in control of the Kremlin. The result, in any case, is that a cash cow—and still the town's livelihood—has passed from the hands of a Moscow oligarch into the hands of the Kremlin.

When I show up in town, Sergey Burov has been mayor for four months. He was once a deputy director for Rosneft and before that a senior manager for Yukos. He, too, is no stranger to violence: In 2005, while walking to his car in the morning, he took a bullet to the stomach. It

Forty years ago Surgut was a collection of wooden hovels, in a place where severe winter lasts four months. Today it is one of Siberia's largest cities, with 300,000 people.

looked like another contract job, but prosecutors closed the case without finding a culprit.

Burov is a burly man whose wide shoulders stretch his suit. He is interested in talking about the town's future, not its bloody past. In partnership with Rosneft, he tells me, the city administration has ambitious plans to redevelop Nefteyugansk. Come back in two years, he says, and I will see an entirely different town, maybe even a yacht club. After the interview his press secretary shows off an indoor sports facility with an Olympic-size swimming pool. In the central plaza, the one littered with pipe just a few days earlier, workers are starting to install brick walkways and flower beds.

Are things finally looking up for Nefteyugansk? Residents seem skeptical. "Maybe Rosneft feels better being here," Vasily Voroshilov, a 52-year-old oil well repairman, says. "But we don't feel it."

That skepticism is shared by many observers outside Russia, who say it's one thing to seize control of an oil company and quite another to run it. Says one analyst of the Kremlin's takeover of Russian oil, "You can steal a Chevy, but that doesn't mean you know how to drive it."

FOR ALL THE WEALTH that oil can produce, it is often as much a curse as a blessing for countries such as Russia. Early in the 1990s, before the oil boom, Boris Yeltsin encouraged local provinces to grab what autonomy they could. This was when Russia's potential for political pluralism and Western-style grassroots democracy looked greatest. When oil prices rose toward the end of the decade, the Kremlin realized that this source of wealth could be used to bring about a humiliated Russia's global resurgence. Salvation by oil has since become an article of national faith.

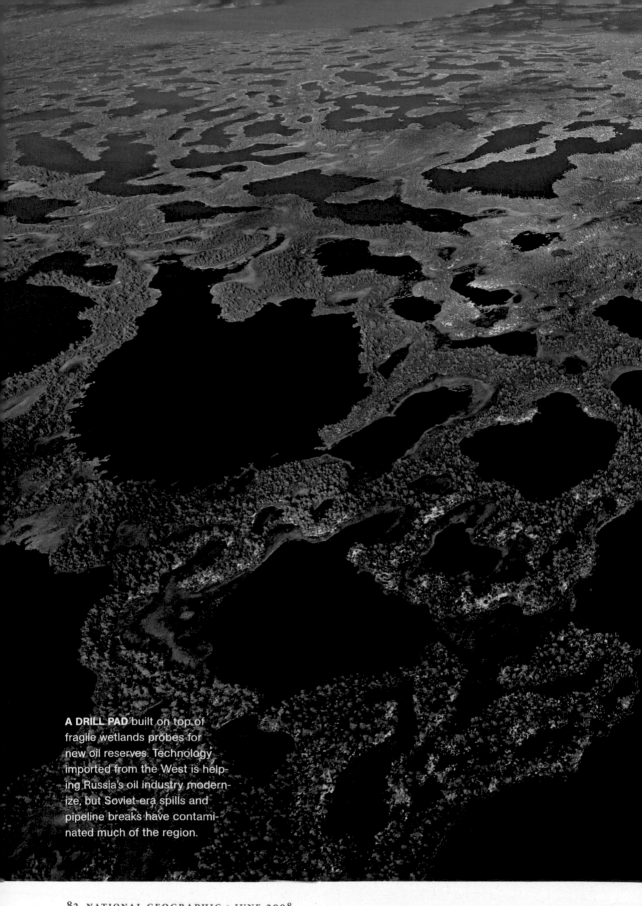

A DRILL PAD built on top of fragile wetlands probes for new oil reserves. Technology imported from the West is helping Russia's oil industry modernize, but Soviet-era spills and pipeline breaks have contaminated much of the region.

HEROIC OIL, sculpted in bronze and titled "Drop of Life," stands in Kogalym. It was given to the city by Lukoil, Russia's largest private oil company, in 2001, the tenth anniversary of the company's founding. While tolerating private firms, the national government is tightening its control of the industry, worrying some experts. Still, from the sleek interior of a well control center at the South Yagunskoye field, Lukoil's future, like that of Russia's new economy, seems bright—for now.

"Oil," said a 16-year-old student at Khanty-Mansiysk's school for math whizzes, "is the only way for our country to stand up, to survive." Actually, there are many ways that the Russians, a creative and educated people, can revive their country. But oil suggests national potency, and Russia's petroleum patrimony lends itself to patriotic incantations of an almost mystical kind. At the festivities on Oilers' Day one of the songs, a salute to the collective might of the neftyaniki, proclaimed, "We are the fingers pressed tightly into a fist."

"Russia's superpower status today comes from energy, not its military," says Julia Nanay, a senior director at PFC Energy, a global consultancy based in Washington, D.C. "The Kremlin determines what happens with oil in western Siberia. They want to control production and exports in order to maximize Russia's geopolitical relevance."

Just as the tsars of old exercised monopolies on valuable commodities such as fur and salt, the Kremlin wants direct control over oil—and over the oligarchs who produce it. Those who come to heel survive; those who don't risk suffering Khodorkovsky's fate, or worse.

One of the survivors is Vagit Alekperov, president of Russia's biggest private oil company, Lukoil. Starting out working on the rigs near his native Baku, Alekperov was sent to Siberia in the late 1970s to manage an oil-production team. A notoriously strict paternalist, he angered his men by banning the sale of alcohol in the village. Several of them grabbed hunting rifles and fired shots at his cabin, but Alekperov, ever the survivor, wasn't there at the time.

During the final days of the Soviet Union, Alekperov forged Lukoil from prime oil assets in western Siberia. Today the company is a global multinational with hydrocarbon reserves second only to ExxonMobil—and some 2,000 gas stations in the U.S. Though most of Lukoil's reserves are in western Siberia, Alekperov keeps his headquarters just two miles from the Kremlin. Like other survivors, he knows that he must be attentive to any change in political mood that could affect Lukoil's fortunes, for better or worse.

A distinguished-looking man with bronze skin and a crop of steel gray hair, Alekperov dresses in impeccably tailored suits. A tough guy, he can also charm. When pressed on

> **"Russia's superpower status today comes from energy, not its military. The Kremlin determines what happens with oil in western Siberia."**
> —JULIA NANAY, ANALYST

whether oil consumers around the world should feel comfortable now that Russia has a large finger on the globe's petroleum tap, he leaned back in his chair, smiled expansively, and asked, "Do I look like a bear?" I couldn't help laughing. "We just want to make money."

Having gobbled up Yukos, might the Kremlin want to swallow Lukoil next? "I don't think either the government or the president of Russia will target such a company," Alekperov remonstrates. I decide not to mention that Khodorkovsky had told me the same thing not long before his arrest.

Lukoil's base of operations in Khanty-Mansi is the town of Kogalym. A roadside floral arrangement spells out the company's name not far from the golden domes of a Russian Orthodox cathedral and the green minaret of a mosque. At a refurbished maternity house— what Russians call a *roddom*—Dr. Galina Pustovit, director of the gynecology department, shows off new Western-standard medical equipment. In a country where many women deliver their babies in Soviet-era buildings reeking of sour cabbage and damp concrete, this gleaming facility rates four stars.

When I mention to Pustovit that Russia's oil industry is known for being corrupt, the doctor gives me a sharp look. "This is oil," she says, sweeping a hand around the gynecology ward. "Oilers built this hospital. All of the objects in this city have been built with oil money, including our beautiful boulevard." Don't judge us too harshly, her look says: Life in these parts has never been better. □

➤ **Siberian Spring** See more of Gerd Ludwig's images of Russia's hinterland in the bloom of an oil bonanza at **ngm.com**.

World oil demand is surging as supplies approach their limits.

IN 2000 A SAUDI OIL GEOLOGIST named Sadad I. Al Husseini made a startling discovery. Husseini, then head of exploration and production for the state-owned oil company, Saudi Aramco, had long been skeptical of the oil industry's upbeat forecasts for future production. Since the mid-1990s he had been studying data from the 250 or so major oil fields that produce most of the world's oil. He looked at how much crude remained in each one and how rapidly it was being depleted, then added all the new fields that oil companies hoped to bring on line in coming decades. When he tallied the numbers, Husseini says he realized that many oil experts "were either misreading the global reserves and oil-production data or obfuscating it."

Tapped Out

Where mainstream forecasts showed output rising steadily each year in a great upward curve that kept up with global demand, Husseini's calculations showed output leveling off, starting as early as 2004. Just as alarming, this production plateau would last 15 years at best, after which the output of conventional oil would begin "a gradual but irreversible decline."

That is hardly the kind of scenario we've come to expect from Saudi Aramco, which sits atop the world's largest proven oil reserves—some 260 billion barrels, or roughly a fifth of the world's known crude—and routinely claims that oil will remain plentiful for many more decades. Indeed, according to an industry source, Saudi oil minister Ali al-Naimi took a dim view of Husseini's report, and in 2004 Husseini retired from Aramco to become an industry consultant. But if he is right, a dramatic shift lies just ahead for a world whose critical systems, from defense to transportation to food production, all run on cheap, abundant oil.

Husseini isn't the first to raise the specter

BY PAUL ROBERTS

From a drilling platform off Newfoundland to a bustling gas station in Lianyungang, China, oil addiction is driving us to search farther and spend more for fuel.

of a peak in global oil output. For decades oil geologists have theorized that when half the world's original endowment of oil has been extracted, getting more out of the ground each year will become increasingly difficult, and eventually impossible. Global output, which has risen steadily from fewer than a million barrels a day in 1900 to around 85 million barrels today, will essentially stall. Ready or not, we will face a post-oil future—a future that could be marked by recession and even war, as the United States and other big oil importers jockey for access to secure oil resources.

Forecasts of peak oil are highly controversial—not because anyone thinks oil will last forever, but because no one really knows how much oil remains underground and thus how close we are to reaching the halfway point. So-called oil pessimists contend that a peak is imminent or has actually arrived, as Husseini believes, hidden behind day-to-day fluctuations in production. That might help explain why crude oil prices have been rising steadily and topped a hundred dollars a barrel early this year.

Optimists, by contrast, insist the turning point is decades away, because the world has so much oil yet to be tapped or even discovered, as well as huge reserves of "unconventional" oil, such as the massive tar-sand deposits in western Canada. Optimists also note that in the past, whenever doomsayers have predicted an "imminent" peak, a new oil-field discovery or oil-extraction technology allowed output to keep rising. Indeed, when Husseini first published his forecasts in 2004, he says, optimists dismissed his conclusions "as curious footnotes."

Many industry experts continue to argue that today's high prices are temporary, the result of technical bottlenecks, sharply rising demand

PEAK OIL
How much oil remains in the Earth cannot be known. But even the most optimistic scenarios hold that before mid-century we will hit peak oil, the point at which half the world's supply has been extracted.

from Asia, and a plummeting dollar. "People will run out of demand before they run out of oil," BP's chief economist declared at a meeting early this year. Other optimists, however, are wavering. Not only have oil prices soared to historic levels, but unlike past spikes, those prices haven't generated a surge in new output. Ordinarily, higher prices encourage oil companies to invest more in new exploration technologies and go after difficult-to-reach oil fields. The price surge that followed the Iran-Iraq war in the 1980s, for example, eventually unleashed so much new oil that markets were glutted. But for the past few years, despite a sustained rise in price, global conventional oil output has hovered around 85 million barrels a day, which happens to be just where Husseini's calculations suggested output would begin to level off.

The change is so stark that the oil industry itself has lost some of its cockiness. Last fall, after the International Energy Agency released a forecast showing global oil demand rising more than a third by 2030, to 116 million barrels a day, several oil-company executives voiced doubts that production could ever keep pace. Speaking to an industry conference in London, Christophe de Margerie, head of the French oil giant Total, flatly declared that the "optimistic case" for maximum daily output was 100 million barrels—meaning global demand could outstrip supply before 2020. And in January, Royal Dutch Shell's CEO, Jeroen van der Veer, estimated that "after 2015 supplies of easy-to-access oil and gas will no longer keep up with demand."

To be sure, veteran oilmen like de Margerie and van der Veer don't talk about peak oil in a geologic sense. In their view, political and economic factors above ground, rather than geologic ones below, are the main obstacles to raising output. War-torn Iraq is said to have huge underground oil reserves, yet because of poor security, it produces about a fifth as much

Paul Roberts is author of The End of Oil, *published in 2004. His new book,* The End of Food, *will be out this summer from Houghton Mifflin Harcourt.*

Oil Futures

After geologist M. King Hubbert correctly predicted that U.S. oil production would peak by the early 1970s, analysts adapted his mathematical formula to calculate the peak of world oil. Forecasts vary widely, but there is agreement that once oil peaks, extracting what remains will be vastly more difficult and costly.

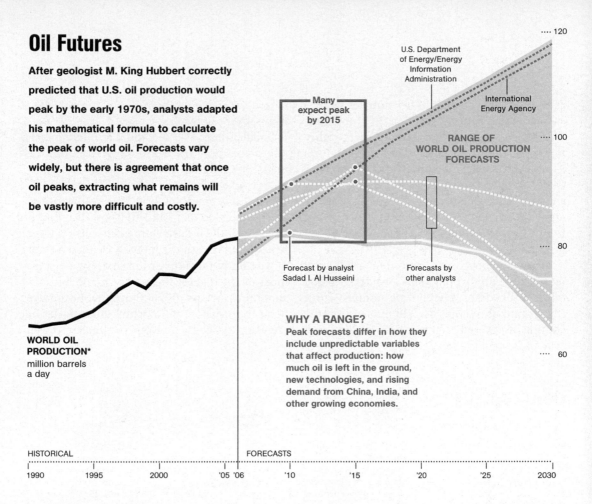

U.S. Department of Energy/Energy Information Administration

International Energy Agency

RANGE OF WORLD OIL PRODUCTION FORECASTS

Many expect peak by 2015

Forecast by analyst Sadad I. Al Husseini

Forecasts by other analysts

WORLD OIL PRODUCTION*
million barrels a day

WHY A RANGE?
Peak forecasts differ in how they include unpredictable variables that affect production: how much oil is left in the ground, new technologies, and rising demand from China, India, and other growing economies.

HISTORICAL   FORECASTS

1990   1995   2000   '05 '06   '10   '15   '20   '25   2030

···· 120
···· 100
···· 80
···· 60

Draining the Reliable Giants

More than a third of the world's oil comes from large fields, relatively easy to tap.
But discovery of new giants, and average production for each field, has declined for decades.
The largest single producer remains a Saudi Arabia megagiant found in the 1940s.

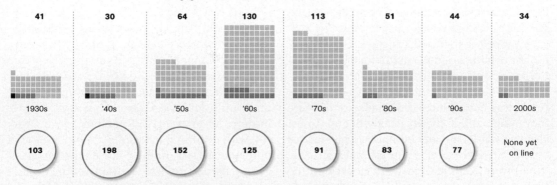

LARGE OIL-FIELD DISCOVERIES
▪ **Giant:** 500 million to 5 billion barrels
▪ **Supergiant:** 5 billion to 50 billion barrels
▪ **Megagiant:** Over 50 billion barrels

41	30	64	130	113	51	44	34
1930s	'40s	'50s	'60s	'70s	'80s	'90s	2000s
103	198	152	125	91	83	77	None yet on line

CURRENT AVERAGE PRODUCTION PER FIELD   thousands of barrels a day

*WORLD OIL PRODUCTION INCLUDES CRUDE OIL, NATURAL GAS PLANT LIQUIDS, OTHER LIQUIDS, AND REFINERY PROCESSING GAINS OR LOSSES.

HIRAM HENRIQUEZ, NG STAFF
SOURCES: BRITISH PETROLEUM; M. K. HORN; NATIONAL PETROLEUM COUNCIL; PEAK OIL NETHERLANDS FOUNDATION

as Saudi Arabia does. And in countries such as Venezuela and Russia, foreign oil companies face restrictive laws that hamper their ability to develop new wells and other infrastructure. "The issue over the medium term is not whether there is oil to be produced," says Edward Morse, a former State Department oil expert who now analyzes markets for Lehman Brothers, "but rather how to overcome political obstacles to production."

Yet even oil optimists concede that physical limits are beginning to loom. Consider the issue of discovery rates. Oil can't be pumped from the ground until it has been found, and yet the volume discovered each year has steadily fallen

Ghawar, which held about 120 billion barrels at its discovery in 1948.

Smaller fields also cost more to operate than larger ones do. "The world has zillions of little fields," says Matt Simmons, a Houston investment banker who has studied the oil discovery trend. "But the problem is, you need a zillion oil rigs to get at them all." This cost disparity is one reason the industry prefers to rely on large fields—and why they supply more than a third of our daily output. Unfortunately, because most of the biggest finds were made decades ago, much of our oil is coming from mature fields that are now approaching their peaks, or are even in decline; output is plummeting in

Other options

As liquid oil becomes more costly and hard to find, researchers ...and entrepreneurs are searching for ways to squeeze fuel from alternative sources.

BIOFUELS
Renewable fuels made from grains, stalks, and plant oils may help offset some of our oil appetite. Already, corn-based ethanol is a popular but controversial additive to gasoline.

COAL TO OIL
Under great pressure and high temperatures, coal—a relatively abundant resource—can be liquefied into fuel. But the process remains expensive and emits large amounts of carbon dioxide.

TAR SANDS
Tar can be extracted from the sands, found in large deposits in western Canada, and turned into crude oil. The process requires huge amounts of water and energy, often from natural gas.

since the early 1960s—despite dazzling technological advances, including computer-assisted seismic imaging that allows companies to "see" oil deep below the Earth's surface. One reason for the decline is simple mathematics: Most of the big, easily located fields—the so-called "elephants"—were discovered decades ago, and the remaining fields tend to be small. Not only are they harder to find than big fields, but they must also be found in greater numbers to produce as much oil. Last November, for example, oil executives were ecstatic over the discovery off the Brazilian coast of a field called Tupi, thought to be the biggest find in seven years. And yet with as much as eight billion barrels, Tupi is about a fifteenth the size of Saudi Arabia's legendary

once prolific regions such as the North Sea and Alaska's North Slope.

Worldwide, output from existing fields is falling by as much as 8 percent a year, which means that oil companies must develop up to seven million barrels a day in additional capacity simply to keep current output steady—plus many more millions of barrels to meet the growth in demand of about 1.5 percent a year. And yet, with declining field sizes, rising costs, and political barriers, finding those new barrels is getting harder and harder. Many of the biggest oil companies, including Shell and Mexico's state-owned Pemex, are actually finding less oil each year than they sell.

As more and more existing fields mature,

Bright as a bull's-eye, a tanker cruises the English Channel. As the struggle for oil intensifies, experts worry crucial infrastructure, including pipelines, rigs, and ships, could provide easy targets for terrorists.

and as global oil demand continues to grow, the deficit will widen substantially. By 2010, according to James Mulva, CEO of ConocoPhillips, nearly 40 percent of the world's daily oil output will have to come from fields that have not been tapped—or even discovered. By 2030 nearly all our oil will come from fields not currently in operation. Mulva, for one, isn't sure enough new oil can be pumped. At a conference in New York last fall, he predicted output would stall at 100 million barrels a day—the same figure Total's chief had projected. "And the reason," Mulva said, "is, where is all that going to come from?"

Whatever the ceiling turns out to be, one prediction seems secure: The era of cheap oil is behind us. If the past is any guide, the world may be in for a rough ride. In the early 1970s, during the Arab oil embargo, U.S. policymakers considered desperate measures to keep oil supplies flowing, even drawing up contingency plans to seize Middle Eastern oil fields.

Washington backed away from military action then, but such tensions are likely to reemerge. Since Saudi Arabia and other members of the Organization of Petroleum Exporting Countries control 75 percent of the world's total oil reserves, their output will peak substantially later than that of other oil regions, giving them even more power over prices and the world economy. A peak or plateau in oil production will also mean that, with rising population, the amount of gasoline, kerosene, and diesel available for each person on the planet may be significantly less than it is today. And if that's bad news for energy-intensive economies, such as the United States, it could be disastrous for the developing world, which relies on petroleum fuels not just for transport but also for cooking, lighting, and irrigation.

Husseini worries that the world has been slow to wake up to the prospect. Fuel-efficient cars and alternatives such as biofuels will compensate for some of the depleted oil supplies, but the bigger challenge may be inducing oil-hungry societies to curb demand. Any meaningful discussion about changes in our energy-intensive lifestyles, says Husseini, "is still off the table." With the inexorable arithmetic of oil depletion, it may not stay off the table much longer. ◻

➤ **After Oil** What fuels will drive the world economy if rising demand for oil outpaces supply? Find out more at **ngm.com**.

livingcolor

Toxic nudibranchs—soft, seagoing
slugs—produce a brilliant defense.

PHOTOGRAPHS BY DAVID DOUBILET

NEMBROTHA KUBARYANA · 2.4 INCHES (6 CENTIMETERS)

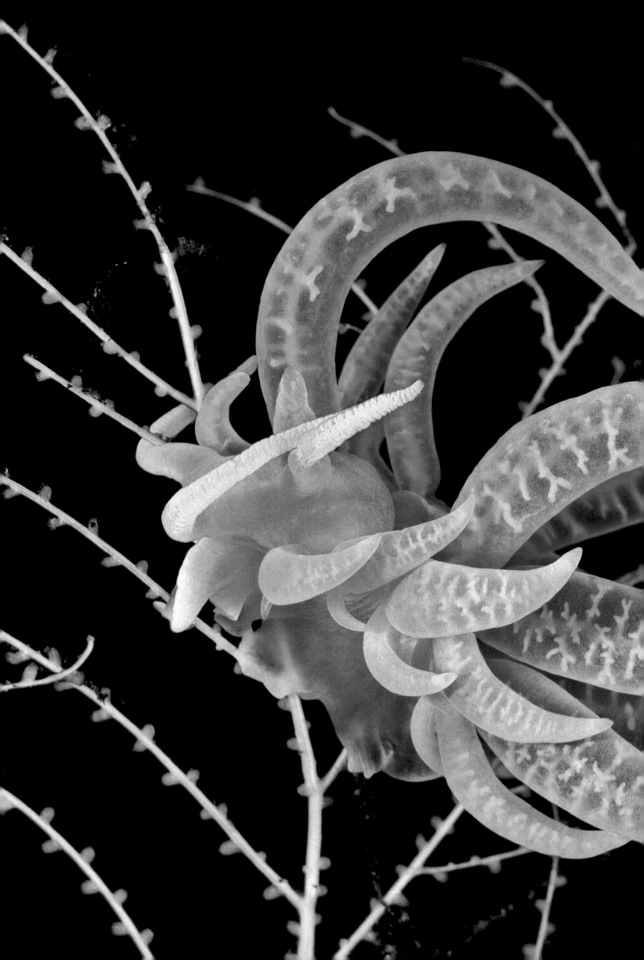

Built to feed exclusively on corals like this spindly gorgonian, a translucent 1.7-inch-long *Phyllodesmium iriomotense* houses its branching digestive gland within tentacle-like cerata—outgrowths the animal can shed if under attack. This species is one of the few colorless nudibranchs.

Nudibranchs crawl through life as slick and naked as a newborn.

Snail kin whose ancestors shrugged off the shell millions of years ago, they are just skin, muscle, and organs sliding on trails of slime across ocean floors and coral heads the world over.

Found from sandy shallows and reefs to the murky seabed nearly a mile down, nudibranchs thrive in waters both warm and cold and even around billowing deep-sea vents. Members of the gastropod class, and more broadly the mollusks, the mostly finger-size morsels live fully exposed, their gills forming tufts on their backs. (Nudibranch means "naked gill," a feature that separates them from other sea slugs.) Although they can release their muscular foothold to tumble in a current—a few can even swim freely—they are rarely in a hurry.

So why, in habitats swirling with voracious eaters, aren't nudibranchs picked off like shrimp at a barbecue? The 3,000-plus known nudibranch species, it turns out, are well equipped to defend themselves. Not only can they be tough-skinned, bumpy, and abrasive, but they've also traded the family shell for less burdensome weaponry: toxic secretions and stinging cells. A few make their own poisons, but most pilfer from the foods they eat. Species that dine on toxic sponges, for example, alter and store the irritating compounds in their bodies and secrete them from skin cells or glands when disturbed. Other nudibranchs hoard capsules of tightly coiled stingers, called nematocysts, ingested from fire corals, anemones, and hydroids. Immune to the sting, the slugs deploy the stolen artillery along their own extremities.

Many mobile nudibranchs—vulnerable as they move in daylight between feeding spots—announce their weapons with garish colors and designs, a palette millions of years in the making. Contrasting pigments make them highly visible against a reef's greens and browns, a visual alarm that turns predators wary—bold nibblers quickly learn to avoid the color patterns that announce unpalatable flesh. Animals able to mimic the designs, including nontoxic nudibranchs and other invertebrates like flatworms, are similarly left alone.

More reclusive nudibranchs, with nocturnal habits or small ranges, may opt for camouflage, from drab to brilliant, rather than contrast (although many of these, too, have toxic defenses). Pigments matching sponges and other edible substrates on which they linger can make even the biggest slug varieties—the length of a man's forearm—vanish where they lie.

Even the most keen-eyed diver may miss those cryptic species. But the brazen ones pop into view in bursts of Crayola colors, one munching coral, another glomming on to a rock face, a third riding a current along the seabed. A lucky sighting is a mass aggregation of dozens or even hundreds gathered at a food-rich locale to feed and mate, or a plate-size "solar powered" species that gets nutrients from photosynthetic algae farmed within its body.

Nudibranchs are blind to their own beauty, their tiny eyes discerning little more than light and dark. Instead the animals smell, taste, and feel their world using head-mounted sensory appendages called rhinophores and oral tentacles. Chemical signals help them track food—

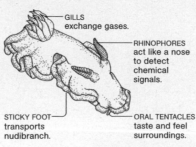

Anatomy of a Nudibranch (*Glossodoris averni*)

GILLS exchange gases.

RHINOPHORES act like a nose to detect chemical signals.

STICKY FOOT transports nudibranch.

ORAL TENTACLES taste and feel surroundings.

ART BY MARIEL FURLONG, NG STAFF

Bornella anguilla flees danger by folding in its appendages and swimming like an eel. 2.8 IN (7 CM)

not just coral and sponges but barnacles, eggs, or small fish—and one another. Hermaphroditic, nudibranchs have both male and female organs and can fertilize one another, an ability that speeds the search for mates and doubles reproductive success. Depending on the species, pairs may lay eggs in coils, ribbons, or tangled clumps, up to two million at a time.

Not all adult encounters have such a fruitful outcome. Sometimes one nudibranch eats the other, particularly if it is of another species. A cannibal slug rears up like a cobra to engulf its kin, using jaws and teeth to finish the job. Other nudibranchs rely on enzymes, rather than teeth, to break down prey. What else can devour a nudibranch without ill consequence? Certain fish, sea spiders, turtles, sea stars, a few crabs. Some people consume them as well, after removing the toxic organs. Chileans and islanders off Russia and Alaska roast or boil sea slugs or eat them raw. (Photographer David Doubilet likened the experience to "chewing an eraser.")

Humans have also studied sea slugs' simple nervous systems for clues to learning and memory and have raided their chemical armory in search of pharmaceuticals. Fashioning remedies from marine invertebrates has a long history: Pliny the Elder, for example, wrote in the first century A.D. of using ground snails mixed with honey to treat "ulcerations of the head" and sea urchin ashes for baldness. Scientists today are isolating chemicals that may help ailing heart, bone, and brain. A sea hare (cousin to the nudibranch) recently offered up a cancer-fighting compound that made it into clinical trials.

Still, nudibranchs have hardly given up all their secrets. Scientists estimate that they've identified only half of all nudibranch species, and even the known ones are elusive. Most live no more than a year and then disappear without a trace, their boneless, shell-less bodies leaving no record of their brief, brilliant lives.

—*Jennifer S. Holland, NG Staff*

David Doubilet found these creatures in Indonesia, photographing them where they lay or on a white background before returning them unharmed. Learn more in Inside Geographic, page 152.

GLOSSODORIS AVERNI · 2.4 IN (6 CM)

ASTERONOTUS CESPITOSUS · 8.7 IN (22 CM)

FLABELLINA EXOPTATA · 1.2 IN (3 CM)

CUTHONA SP. · 0.7 IN (1.8 CM)

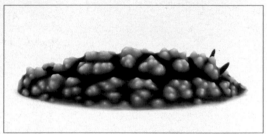

PHYLLIDIELLA PUSTULOSA · 2.4 IN (6 CM)

THECACERA PACIFICA · 2.4 IN (6 CM)

JORUNNA FUNEBRIS · 2 IN (5 CM)

PHYLLIDIA OCELLATA · 2.4 IN (6 CM)

HYPSELODORIS SP. · 2 IN (5 CM)

MEXICHROMIS MARIEI · 1.2 IN (3 CM)

CHROMODORIS DIANAE · 2.4 IN (6 CM)

PTERAEOLIDIA IANTHINA · 5.9 IN (15 CM)

NEMBROTHA CRISTATA · 4.7 IN (12 CM)

Chromodoris annae compensate for their tiny size with loud, contrasting hues—warning predators of a toxic snack.

0.8 IN (2 CM)

CERATOSOMA GRACILLIMUM · 4.7 IN (12 CM)

CHROMODORIS GEOMETRICA · 1 IN (2.5 CM)

GODIVA SP. · 1.6 IN (4 CM)

Breeding and Feeding
Inch-long *Hypselodoris whitei* (above) mate head to tail through a genital aperture. Equipped with both male and female reproductive organs—as are all nudibranchs—each fertilizes the other, and both produce eggs. *H. kanga* (right), 1.6 inches long, uses its sticky foot to secure an egg ribbon extruded from an oviduct on its side; hatchlings by the thousands will soon disperse with the currents. As adults, nudibranchs can be finicky eaters: A zebra-striped species of *Armina* (below), a genus that ranges to 8 inches long, plays tug-of-war with its sole prey, the burrowing sea pen. A tiny blenny bystander picks the safer perch.

A hard body and thick skin help armor *Halgerda batangas* against predators. Any that persist learn that the sponge-eater also exudes a toxin. 1.6 IN (4 CM)

Out
of the
Shadows

The elusive Central Asian
snow leopard steps into
a risk-filled future.

Snow leopards don't care much for
company. So to get close, photographer Steve Winter deployed a series
of camera traps that automatically
snapped pictures whenever an animal
crept near. The result is a set of inti-
mate portraits that expands our vision
of a legendary mountain recluse.

Rub, scratch, urinate, defecate—a snow leopard marks its trail with often pungent graffiti. The scent helps these solitary cats avoid confrontation in territory they share. During mating season, though, the scent is meant as a magnet. As few as 3,500 of these endangered cats may survive in the wild.

To traverse rocky slopes and survive in cold mountain climes—even at altitudes as high as 18,000 feet—snow leopards are well equipped. Long hair with thick underfur, wide, well-padded paws, and a big chest and strong lungs keep these cats running up where the air gets thin.

during social encounters or to wrap partway around itself like a scarf when bedded down in bitter weather. But the main function of this plume is to add balance in an environment with thousand-foot drops.

In Mongolia a park ranger once told me he'd seen snow leopards crouch and sway that plume in the air to lure curious marmots closer, just as hunters do with white rags. Possible. But I heard a simpler explanation from Sodnomde-leg Bazarhuyag, a retired doctor in a community of herders in northwestern Mongolia. We went to search out snow leopard sign in a gorge glistening with river ice. When a band of scimitar-horned wild goats (ibex) appeared on the sky-line, Bazarhuyag scanned carefully around them, saying, "Snow leopards are good at hiding, but sometimes they forget about their tail."

DARKNESS CLAIMS the last crags. Raghu and I won't glimpse a snow leopard this day. It's not a disappointment. The great cat is only living up to its reputation for being impossible to find. Called *shan* in Ladakhi, *irbis* in Mongolian, and *barfani chita*—snow cheetah—in Urdu, the carnivore scientists label *Uncia uncia* ranges across about a million square miles and portions of 12 nations. You'll never hear one give away its whereabouts by roaring; it lacks the throat structure, though it can hiss, chuff, mew, growl, and wail. Besides being secretive, well camouflaged, and usually solitary, snow leopards are most active at night and in the twilight hours of dusk and dawn, amid the most formidable tumult of mountains on Earth: the Himalaya and Karakoram; the Plateau of Tibet and adjoining Kunlun; the Hindu Kush, Pamirs, and Tian Shan; the Altay, whose peaks define Mongolia's border with China, Kazakhstan, and Russia; and the Sayan chain west of Lake Baikal.

Bound to high, cold, steep terrain, snow leopards have always remained at fairly low densities, but became still more sparse during the past century because thousands were turned into pelts for the fashion trade. Though officially protected since 1975 under the Convention on International Trade in Endangered Species, the spotted cats continue to be killed

On Pakistan's far northern frontier, a park ranger scans the slopes for wild goats—prime snow leopard prey—as researcher Tom McCarthy (left) sets up a snare beside a tree raked by cat claws. His goal is to capture and radio-collar a cat. "You can spend months in the mountains and not see a snow leopard or even any signs of one," says McCarthy. "But I can feel when they're around."

for their coat, worth a black market fortune. Demand for their bones and penis, hyped as tonics in eastern Asia, is increasing. Conflicts with livestock keep growing too, which leads to more persecution by herders. Bait, snares, pitfall traps, and poisons make it far easier to kill a snow leopard than to see one alive. The current population is estimated at only 4,000 to 7,000. While these aren't hard figures, the number may be less than half of what it was a century ago. Some authorities fear that the actual number may already have slipped below 3,500. Five of the countries in snow leopard range may have 200 or fewer.

There's no escaping the fact that most of the world's big cats are in deep trouble, from

■ **Society Grant** Camera-trap photography for this article was supported by an Expeditions Council grant made possible by your Society membership.

A cat might be moving right now, perfectly silent and perfectly tensed, maybe close by.

the heavily poached tiger to the last 30 free-roaming Amur leopards. Snow leopards are no exception. But here's some encouraging news: the rise of grassroots conservation efforts in a few locales to halt the snow leopard's downward spiral. Several community-based programs in India and Mongolia sounded especially promising—at least on paper. But how well do they really work?

Saving an animal means getting to know it, and scientific information about the leopard is scarce. Perhaps no other large, popular land mammal has so many details of its natural history still missing. Raghu, the regional director of science and conservation for the nonprofit Snow Leopard Trust, knows as much as anyone,

and he has that sixth sense that researchers with years afield develop, an extra awareness that guides him to the fragile leg bones of an infant blue sheep here in a ravine, or an ibex skull lying there, high on a slope where wind whips the wildflowers into blurs of color, and lets him say things like: "At a fresh carcass, you can tell if a snow leopard with young made the kill. The ears will be gnawed off. Those are all the cubs can get at until she opens up the hide for them."

Tall and fit, with a long-legged stride, Raghu is a wizard at trailing faint paw prints across stony ground. But the otherwise ghostlike predators also leave behind a surprising amount of more obvious clues. It helps to picture 80- to 120-pound cats in a colossal litter box.

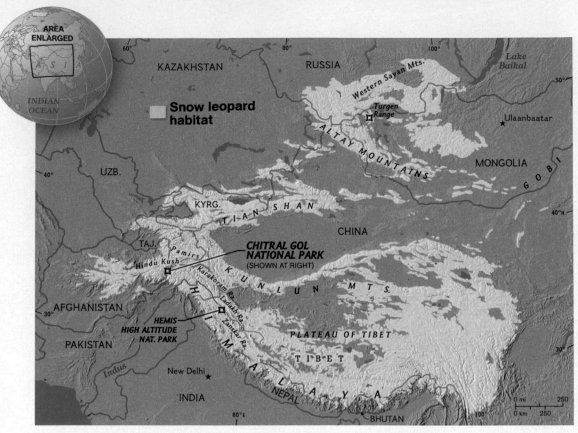

Terrain high enough and rugged enough to serve as potential habitat for snow leopards covers about a million square miles in 12 countries. Much of that range is severely fragmented, and scant resources are dedicated to its protection.

Droppings, together with scrapes made by the rear legs, reveal habitual routes that tend to follow ridgelines or the base of cliffs. Scrambling for footing day after day, I gradually realize that these travelers like to mark the same type of features that draw my attention en route: solitary boulders, sharp corners along gullies, knolls, and saddles. Near tree line, they stripe the occasional trunk with long, vertical claw marks.

If my eyes are too busy taking in scenery to notice a fresh scrape, my nose will still register the acrid tang of leopard pee. Elsewhere, I'll catch a musky aroma sprayed from anal glands up onto an overhanging rock. Frequently used scent posts take on an oily sheen. Passing cats stretch to rub their cheeks against them, leaving white hairs for me to tuck in a pocket for luck scaling the next rock face. Fifteen, sixteen thousand feet, no matter how far up I climb, some villager will have gone higher and left stone cairns bearing prayer flags or stacks of horns. Later, the cats come by and leave their own markings on these offerings. "A lot of research on snow leopard movements really tells you more about the limits of human abilities," says Raghu after crossing a cascade swollen with glacial melt. "You can only climb so many slopes before you grow exhausted or encounter sheer cliffs. It is just not possible to keep up." So Raghu tried capturing the cats to attach radios to them. He finally collared a female. But, like previous investigators, he was seldom able to monitor a signal for long before the animal dropped behind some ridge that blocked the transmission.

Over the years, biologists reported snow leopards covering territories of five to fourteen square miles. But when American biologist Tom McCarthy first placed a satellite collar on one in Mongolia in 1996, he found it roaming 386 square miles. "My guess is that the more satellite collars we get out, the larger we'll discover snow leopard territories to actually be," said McCarthy, now the science and conservation director of Snow Leopard Trust. Ten years passed before the next satellite tag was put on, again by McCarthy, this time in Pakistan. By mid-2007

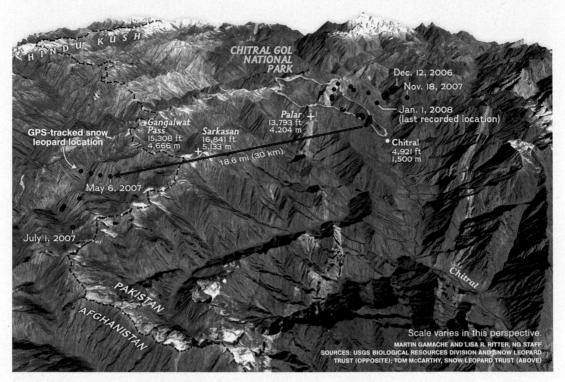

Within the image:

HINDU KUSH

CHITRAL GOL NATIONAL PARK

Dec. 12, 2006
Nov. 18, 2007

Jan. 1, 2008
(last recorded location)

Gangalwat Pass
15,308 ft
4,666 m

Sarkasan
16,841 ft
5,133 m

Palar
13,793 ft
4,204 m

GPS-tracked snow leopard location

Chitral
4,921 ft
1,500 m

18.6 mi (30 km)

May 6, 2007

July 1, 2007

PAKISTAN
AFGHANISTAN

Chitral

Scale varies in this perspective.
MARTIN GAMACHE AND LISA R. RITTER, NG STAFF
SOURCES: USGS BIOLOGICAL RESOURCES DIVISION AND SNOW LEOPARD
TRUST (OPPOSITE); TOM McCARTHY, SNOW LEOPARD TRUST (ABOVE)

Red dots mark the meanderings of one satellite-tracked leopard as it loped between Pakistan and Afghanistan. The tracking collar was meant to send data regularly, but a technical glitch blocked transmissions for several months.

the cat wearing it had revealed its movements over a 115-square-mile area and had moved across the border to Afghanistan.

SNOW LEOPARD RESEARCHERS need to gather more than cat facts, because you can neither understand nor save a predator without doing the same for its prey. Snow leopards hunt chiefly Asia's high-country array of hoofed wildlife: ibex, argali and urial sheep, blue sheep, tahr, the goat-antelopes known as gorals and serows, Tibetan antelope, Tibetan and goitered gazelles, musk deer, red deer, wild boars, wild asses, wild yaks, and wild Bactrian camels. Marmots, hares, and mouse hares (pikas) are on the menu too, along with partridges and turkey-size snow cocks. On top of everything else, snow leopards routinely add the tall, feathery shrub *Myricaria* and other plants to their diet. Curious, but then my house cat swallows grass and loves cantaloupe.

As the top carnivore of the alpine and subalpine zones, the snow leopard strongly influences the numbers and whereabouts of hoofed herds over time. That in turn affects plant communities and thus shapes the niches of many a smaller organism down the food chain. The leopard's presence—or absence—affects competing hunters and scavengers too, namely wolves, wild dogs, jackals, foxes, bears, and lynx. This cascade of consequences makes *Uncia uncia* a governing force in the ecosystem, what scientists term a keystone species.

Since the range of the snow leopard overlaps those of so many other creatures, protecting its habitat also preserves homes for the majority of mountain flora and fauna. While we were exploring part of the Zanskar Range in Ladakh, Raghu and I crossed tracks that sent him racing off to an overlook. A few minutes later, a brown bear—the same species as North America's grizzly—galloped and slid down a high riverbank, swam across surging rapids, muscled halfway up a cliff wall, and finally lay down to dry its silver-tipped fur in the warm morning sun. We had found one of the last few dozen

Crags and crevices in India's Hemis National Park give snow leopards cover when they are hunting, but offer less effective protection from poachers. Wildlife conservationist George Schaller fears the cats might someday only survive in zoos —a fate he calls "a sad compromise."

of its kind in that huge section of the Himalaya.

Do snow leopards attack humans, as bears sometimes do? No, never, Raghu says. He once watched a village girl pulling on one end of a dead goat, unaware that the other end, hidden by a bush, was snagged in a snow leopard's jaws. She came away unscratched. But a single leopard swatfest in a herd of livestock can plunge a family into desperate poverty.

Because farming is marginal at best in Central Asia's cold, dry landscapes, traditional cultures depend mainly upon livestock to get by. Some herders operate from mountainside hamlets. Others are nomadic, migrating long distances between seasonal pastures. Either way, snow leopard conflicts come with the lifestyle. Wired to select the unwary and the stragglers among wild ungulates, the cats can hardly help picking off a few domesticated versions. At night, when flocks are stuffed into low stone corrals, a leopard can all too easily hop in to join them.

During a several-day trek through the Sham area of the Ladakh Range, which rises to the north of the Zanskar Range, on the other side of the Indus River Valley, Jigmet Dadul, a conservationist, and I made our way over the passes to the barley fields and poplar groves of the village of Ang. There we looked up Sonam Namgil. Three

Overgrazing by livestock also reduces the natural capacity of rangelands to support native herds. Hungry leopards turn to the tame flocks for food, and angry herders kill the cats in retaliation. With little or no government enforcement of wildlife regulations in remote areas, a protection strategy has little chance of breaking these cycles unless it gains local support.

Religious leaders have recently spoken up on the leopards' behalf. Within the mountain-ringed courtyard of the Rangdum monastery, between the Zanskar Range and the main Himalaya, Tsering Tundup, a Buddhist monk, said, "Whenever we have an opportunity, we talk to people and encourage them not to kill any being." Several people told me that the villagers listened when a lama farther up the valley condemned a spate of revenge shootings of snow leopards. Soon afterward, a new lotus-shaped shrine was built with the herders' guns cemented inside.

The Dalai Lama, leader of Tibetan Buddhism, who is widely followed in Central Asia, has specifically urged followers to safeguard snow leopards and avoid wearing their pelts as part of traditional festive clothing. "People depend upon animals, but we must not use them for our luxury," he told me during an interview in Washington. "Wild animals are the ornaments of our planet and have every right to exist peacefully. Some, including snow leopards, are quite rare and visible only at high

When Namgil opened the door, he found wide golden eyes staring back.

nights before, a snow leopard had leaped atop his stout mud-brick outbuilding and then ten feet down through a ventilation hole onto the floor. When Namgil opened the door in the morning, he found wide golden eyes staring back amid the bodies of nine goat kids and a sheep.

"The wolf comes and kills, eats, and goes somewhere else," said the 64-year-old herder in a ragged sheepskin coat, "but snow leopards are always around. They have killed one or two animals in the pastures many times. This was the first problem at my home. Everybody wanted to finish this leopard."

The cats may claim only a small part of livestock herds, but the loss may be huge to the owner. Where losses mount, it's often because human hunting has made natural prey scarce.

altitudes. So we need to pay special attention to protect them."

Financial incentives can also make a difference. Jigmet Dadul's employer, Snow Leopard Conservancy–India, had helped set up Himalayan Homestays, a program that steers trekkers to the houses of herders who agree to protect snow leopards and their wild neighbors. For a clean room and bed, meals with the family, and a warm introduction to their culture, visitors pay about ten dollars a night and save carrying a tent and food. Having guests once every couple weeks through the tourist season provides the hosts with more than enough income to replace stock lost to predators.

The conservancy donates funds to cover livestock pens with stout wire mesh. Rodney

Their big eyes are so well adapted for low-light vision that snow leopards can hunt in near total darkness—but they can still go hungry when humans compete for their prey. Though trophy hunts for wild sheep and goats bring income to local communities, they can deplete food stocks for snow leopards.

In fields below the cliffside monastery of Phuktal, Indian farmers harvest barley one fistful at a time. As more people try to eke out a living on higher ground in the Himalaya, they increasingly cross paths with snow leopards traveling down the mountains during winter in pursuit of food, wild or domesticated.

Officials from Kabul guard a crate of artifacts exhibited in Paris, Turin, and Amsterdam before heading to U.S. museums. "These are national treasures," says curator Fredrik Hiebert. "They're not going anywhere without the Afghans." The collection includes a miniature mask of a Greek god (top right).

Omara Khan Massoudi knows how to keep a secret.

Massoudi is director of the National Museum of Afghanistan in Kabul. Like the French citizens during World War II who hid works of art in the countryside to prevent them from falling into Nazi hands, Massoudi and a few trusted *tahilwidars*—key holders—secretly packed away Afghanistan's ancient

treasures when they saw their country descend into an earthly hell.

First came the Soviet invasion in 1979, followed about ten years later by a furious civil war that reduced much of Kabul to ruins. As Afghan warlords battled for control of the city, fighters pillaged the national museum, selling the choicest artifacts on the black market and using museum records to kindle campfires. In 1994 the building was shelled, destroying its roof and top floor. The final assault came in 2001, when teams of hammer-wielding Taliban zealots came to smash works of art they deemed idolatrous. When they finished, more than 2,000 artifacts lay in smithereens.

Throughout those dark years, Massoudi and a handful of other museum officials kept quiet about the hoard of museum artifacts—among them the crown jewels of Afghanistan, the famed Bactrian gold—that they had hidden in vaults under the presidential palace in 1988, as the Soviet occupation gave way to civil war. Researchers the world over despaired of ever seeing the objects again, thinking they'd been sold piecemeal into the illicit antiquities trade or destroyed by the Taliban in their final, iconoclastic frenzy.

Roger Atwood is the author of Stealing History, *an investigation of the antiquities trade. Richard Barnes's latest project looks at the role of museums in society.*

By October 2003—more than two years after U.S.-led forces toppled the Taliban regime—most of the key holders had disappeared or had fled Afghanistan. Massoudi felt it was time to see if the objects had survived the war. When a team of locksmiths wrenched open the safes that month, every last piece of the Bactrian gold was there, trussed in the same tissue paper in which the museum staff had wrapped it. Five months later, researchers opened a set of footlockers stashed in the same underground vault and made another jaw-dropping discovery: priceless 2,000-year-old ivory carvings and glassware that had been excavated in the 1930s from a site known as Begram and given up for lost. Massoudi's staff had cloistered those away too, and they were remarkably well preserved.

"If we had not hidden them, the treasures of Afghanistan would have been lost. That is a fact. Those who knew the truth kept silent," says Massoudi, sipping ginger tea in his spartanly furnished office. His museum—Afghanistan's museum—has been rebuilt with help from UNESCO and other international donors, and it hums with activity now. Exhibit planners stroll from gallery to gallery, taking measurements for future installations; teachers lecture in Dari to groups of schoolgirls in head scarves. At the door, policemen in gray-flannel uniforms keep a close watch. Visitor numbers have inched up to about 6,000 a year. Storerooms are filling with

BRONZE MASK FROM BEGRAM, 3.7 IN (9.5 CM) TALL. FIRST CENTURY A.D.

AFGHAN TREASURES 135

> "If we had not
> hidden them,
> the treasures of
> Afghanistan would
> have been lost.
> That is a fact. Those
> who knew the
> truth kept silent."
>
> —Omara Khan Massoudi
> DIRECTOR, NATIONAL MUSEUM OF AFGHANISTAN

looted artifacts intercepted by customs agents around the world and restituted to Afghanistan, including some 5,000 confiscated artifacts returned from Switzerland and Denmark. More than four tons of loot seized by British police sit in a warehouse in London's Heathrow Airport awaiting repatriation.

In the museum lobby, Massoudi demonstrates what it means to rebuild heritage. Standing in a display case is a life-size statue of a bodhisattva, a type of Buddhist deity, dating from the third century A.D., an era when Afghanistan was a predominantly Buddhist land. Taliban hammers had shattered the fired-clay statue, and museum conservators recently finished reassembling the fragments. A jigsaw of cracks is still visible, but the statue's face again glows with rapturous piety.

"As we finish the restoration of pieces, we bring them out to show the public, one by one. We will be doing this for many years," says Massoudi. Yet the choicest artifacts—the ones he and his staff concealed for so long—won't be on display in Kabul for some time to come. The museum lacks an adequate security system and remains short on staff, while a series of suicide bombings around Kabul have underlined the continuing risks.

Faced with these problems, Afghans have gathered their ancient treasures into a dazzling exhibition and sent it on an international tour. The Afghan government asked National Geographic to inventory the artifacts and help organize the exhibition, which is currently at the National Gallery of Art in Washington, D.C., after a two-year spell in Europe. In addition to

safeguarding the treasures, the Afghans hope the exhibit will elevate the image of their country.

"The history of Afghanistan is one of receiving the arts of others, and then turning them into our own way of expression," says Massoudi. He believes the exhibit will help people see beyond his country's recent history of intolerance and isolation to the open, cosmopolitan spirit that long characterized this creative melting pot and hub of the Silk Road trade.

Walk through the bazaars in Kabul or Mazar-e Sharif and you'll see why, for more than two millennia, people have been calling Afghanistan the crossroads of Asia. One face looks Mediterranean, another Arab—or Indian, or Chinese, or eastern European. Eyes range from pea green to chestnut brown to something approaching orange. Successive invasions and influences wove a tapestry of ethnicities and left behind what the exhibition curator, Fredrik Hiebert of the National Geographic Society, calls "some of the most remarkable archaeological finds in all of Central Asia."

THE ANCIENT CITY of Begram supplied many of the luminous objects. Today Soviet-era land mines litter its grassy landscape, and American fighter jets from a nearby air base howl overhead. But 2,000 years ago this was the opulent summer capital of the great Kushan Empire, which stretched as far as northern India. Traders brought ivories and art from all corners of Asia. Courtiers stuffed themselves on local figs, pomegranates, and grapes against the majestic scrim of the snowy Hindu Kush.

When French archaeologists cut into the site in the late 1930s, they found a cache of luxury goods suggesting a vibrant, trade-based economy that flourished while Rome crumbled. Buried under layers of soil were bronze sculptures from Italy, lacquer boxes from China, plaster medallions of muscular Greek youths, and a group of exquisitely painted Egyptian glass vessels depicting, among other things, the Alexandria lighthouse, an African leopard hunt, and a scene from the *Iliad*. Most strikingly, the diggers found stacks upon stacks of carved

Where trading communities once prospered, researchers know much remains to be discovered—and thieves do too. Nadir Rassouli, director of the Afghan Institute of Archaeology, inspects a looter's hole near Paghman with some of the 500 national police recently assigned to protect more than 1,500 ancient sites.

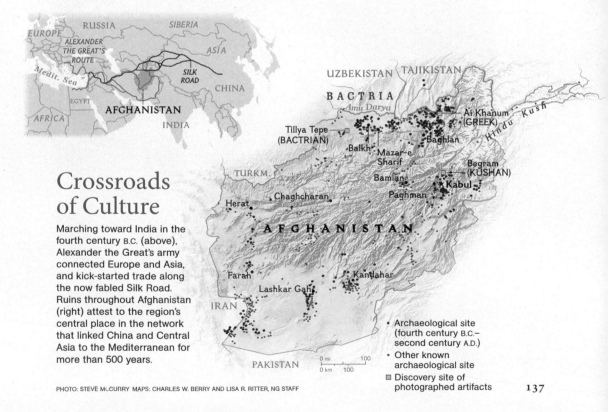

Crossroads of Culture

Marching toward India in the fourth century B.C. (above), Alexander the Great's army connected Europe and Asia, and kick-started trade along the now fabled Silk Road. Ruins throughout Afghanistan (right) attest to the region's central place in the network that linked China and Central Asia to the Mediterranean for more than 500 years.

- Archaeological site (fourth century B.C.– second century A.D.)
- Other known archaeological site
- Discovery site of photographed artifacts

PHOTO: STEVE McCURRY MAPS: CHARLES W. BERRY AND LISA R. RITTER, NG STAFF

Foreign luxuries passed through Afghanistan on their way to other places, while local artists produced coveted things of beauty as well. The handle of a dagger (left) from a nomad's burial at Tillya Tepe—with imaginary beasts on the shaft and a Siberian bear at the top—was likely made from native gold and turquoise. A plaster medallion of a youth, viewed here through an exhibit window, was uncovered at Begram along with other Greek-style figures. All

LIMESTONE FOUNTAIN SPOUT, 8.3 IN (21 CM) TALL. SECOND CENTURY B.C.

ABOVE: FISH-SHAPED GLASS VESSEL, 7.9 IN (20 CM) LONG. RIGHT: GOLD ROBE ORNAMENT SET WITH TURQUOISE, GARNET, AND PYRITE, 11.5 IN (29.1 CM) LONG. BOTH FIRST CENTURY A.D.

Diverse artifacts offer glimpses into life in antiquity. A gold collar inlaid with gems (right) was sewn to the robe of a noblewoman buried at Tillya Tepe. She and her fellow nomads probably wore their finery wherever they went. A stone gargoyle from Ai Khanum (top left) spouted water at a fountain where people may have bathed after visiting a nearby gymnasium. A glass flask in the shape of a fish (left) survived a long journey to Begram from Egypt, then lay buried for centuries in the ruins of what experts now believe was a merchant's warehouse.

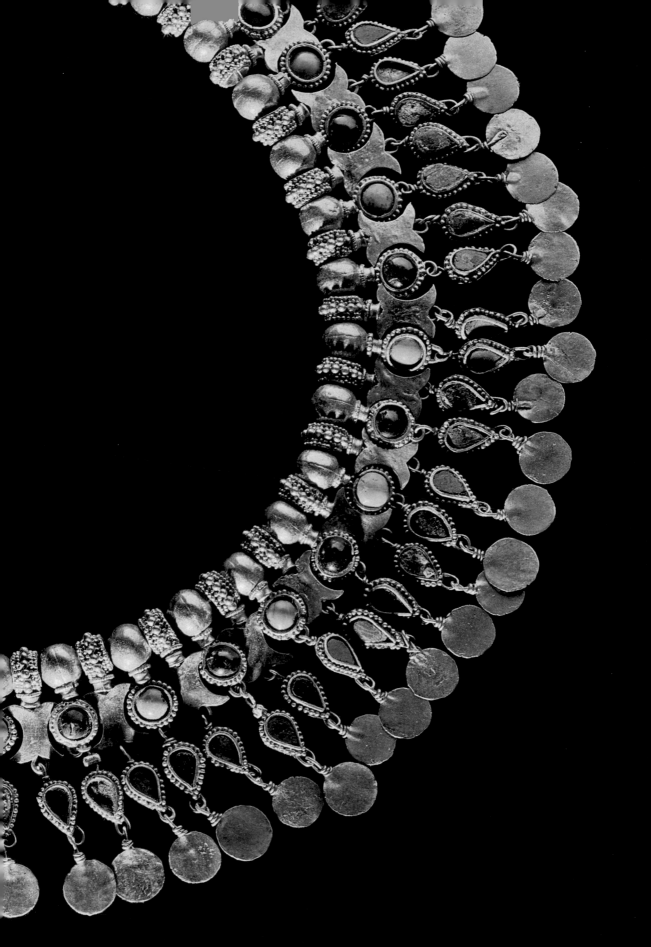

Storerooms are filling with looted artifacts intercepted by customs agents around the world. More than four tons of loot sit in a warehouse in London's Heathrow Airport awaiting repatriation.

ivory and bone sculptures, more than a thousand in all, featuring placidly smiling women and mythical river creatures associated with the art of India.

Someone left this impossibly eclectic mix inside two rooms that, around A.D. 200, were bricked shut and abandoned. Dazzled by the find, archaeologists compared it to the discovery of King Tut's tomb 15 years earlier, believing it to be the remains of a royal residence. Researchers now think the structure may have been a warehouse for luxury goods being transported across Asia on the Silk Road or marketed to local elites.

Like Begram, the site of Tillya Tepe ("golden hill") in Afghanistan's northwestern corner yielded treasures—most famously the Bactrian gold—whose legend was only heightened when they disappeared from view. Found by Russian archaeologist Viktor Sarianidi in the 1970s, the hoard tells a uniquely Afghan story of how nomads rode off the Central Asian steppes around the time of Christ, crossed the Amu Darya River, and created a civilization whose art reflects an amalgam of East and West, transience and settled life. From the wilds of Siberia come the animals, such as a bear depicted on a knife handle, dancing and holding a grapevine in its mouth. Greek and Hindu influences merge in a golden Aphrodite with wings and an Indian-style circle on her forehead.

Many objects show a strikingly Western naturalism, such as a ram sculpted in gold that decorated a nomad nobleman's headdress. Only under a magnifying glass can the masterpiece's splendid workmanship be fully appreciated. And

a delicate, golden crown tells of a refined culture that had not given up its steppes roots. The crown can be disassembled into six pieces for easy transport, perhaps in a leather satchel on a two-humped Bactrian camel—a perfect accessory for a nomadic princess.

ARCHAEOLOGY IS SLOWLY returning to Afghanistan, promising more discoveries and deeper knowledge. New sites are being excavated, and well-known ones are being mapped for reexploration. In the past, American or European researchers played key roles; these days, Afghan archaeologists often lead projects on their own.

On a steep hillside outside Kabul, at a well-preserved Buddhist site from about A.D. 400 called Tepe Maranjan, Afghan researchers found the remains of 16 clay bodhisattvas arranged in a circle. Only their feet and the bottom of their robes were intact, and the Buddha statue they'd once surrounded was gone, probably demolished in the first Islamic invasions a few centuries later. Also gone, except for its bare feet, was a 20-foot-tall upright Buddha that had towered over the site, beckoning the monks to prayer. Perched on an arid hilltop, overlooking the plains where today the city of Kabul stands, the site gives a rich sense of the Buddhist ideals of quiet contemplation and remove.

"If this had been discovered during the Taliban's day, it might well have been destroyed," says archaeologist Najib Sedeqi. A few guards keep a close eye on the site with cooperation from neighbors.

Every period in the country's history is opening up to exploration. Afghan and French archaeologists will soon start excavating one of the oldest known mosques in Afghanistan, the No Gonbad ("nine domes"), which stands outside Balkh amid fields of flourishing marijuana plants. With its mighty columns and thick walls, now half-buried in soil and debris, the mosque expresses power and permanence. When Islam came to Afghanistan, it clearly came to stay.

Despite the progress, huge challenges remain. Crime, looting, and the threat posed by Taliban

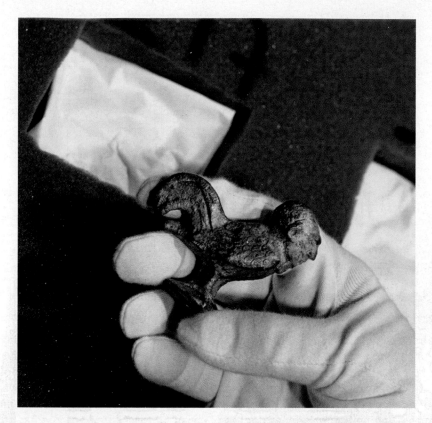

Mystery in bronze: Carefully packed for travel between exhibitions, a human-headed rooster figure puzzles experts. Was it a weight used on merchants' scales? What does the figure represent? Investigating such questions has been impossible in the decades of violence that have wracked Afghanistan.

insurgents could snuff out Afghanistan's nascent cultural revival at any moment. At Tillya Tepe villagers looking for antiquities and building material have practically leveled the "golden hill." At Ai Khanum, where Alexander the Great built a city on the banks of the Amu Darya, archaeologists found baths, Hellenic lettering, and other traces of an outpost of Greek culture on the doorstep of China. Since then, unemployed fighters for local warlords have started to pillage the site, turning it into a lunar landscape of pits and tunnels. At Begram, looters who were once moonlight scavengers have become bolder and better equipped.

"We were patrolling the site one evening when we heard a gunshot, and then I realized that we were the target," said Aynadin Sodeqi, the mustachioed commander of the Begram unit of a new police force charged with protecting Afghan archaeological sites.

He and his men had stumbled upon a group of looters who were digging treasures to sell in the antiquities trade. The looters escaped, but Sodeqi and his men found at least part of their stash: 28 ancient coins and a stone tablet decorated with lotus flowers. Sodeqi also found a piece of equipment that the looters presumably planned to use that evening. What kind of equipment? He answered with a pantomime, holding out his fists and vibrating them up and down: a jackhammer.

"The looters know the value of the things

BRONZE ROOSTER FIGURE FROM BEGRAM, 2.1 IN (5.4 CM) TALL. FIRST CENTURY A.D.

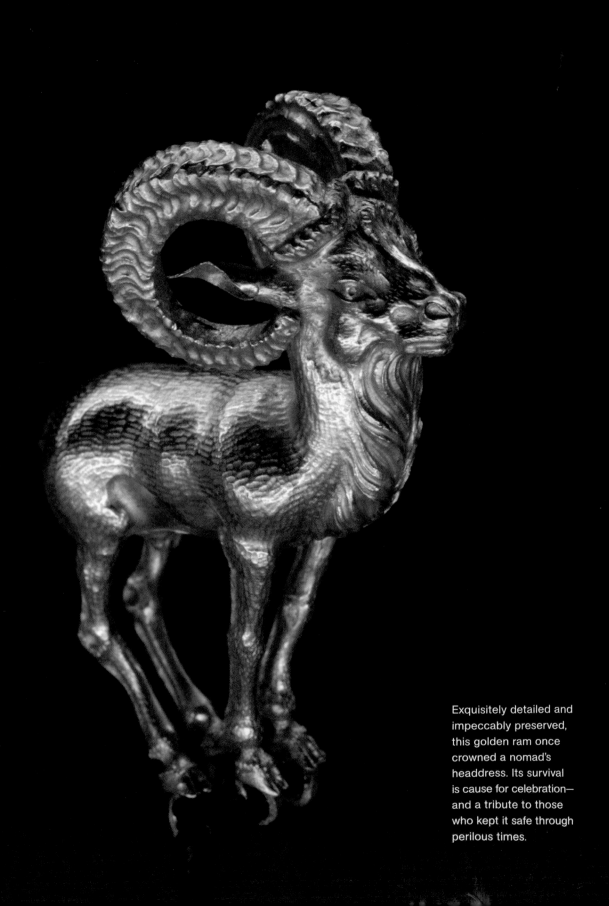

Exquisitely detailed and impeccably preserved, this golden ram once crowned a nomad's headdress. Its survival is cause for celebration—and a tribute to those who kept it safe through perilous times.

they pillage," says Nadir Rassouli, director of the Afghan government's Institute of Archaeology, which has final authority over the country's 1,500-plus known ancient sites. "They are armed, and no matter how many officers we place at sites, they attack them and drive them off. Then they loot."

At Rassouli's prodding, the Afghan government created the archaeology police force in 2004, starting with about 200 men. It has grown to 500, but Rassouli says it would take many times that number to cover the entire country. Most lack training and weapons. The first sustained attack on the new force came in August 2006 at the legendary Silk Road outpost of Balkh, whose towering walls protect the remains of millennia of history. Four officers were killed by antiquities hunters in that incident, and at least six more have since been murdered in the line of duty.

Tons of Afghan loot are believed to be circulating globally. Coins have a particularly avid market, and Begram has long been known for huge caches embedded in its soil, attesting to its role as a major trading point in antiquity. A British traveler in 1833 reported that local people dug up 30,000 coins every year. He carried off 2,000 for himself.

Today it is land mines that stud Begram's fields, as members of Sodeqi's police unit know. Among protruding sherds of Kushan-era pottery, lines of red stones mark the dangers; a closer look reveals innocent-looking plastic disks lurking in the grass like discarded toys. Such is the poverty and desperation—and such are the profits to be gained from antiquities—that not even land mines deter looters.

LAND MINES, a resurgent Taliban, suicide bombs, the searing memory of war—the obstacles bedeviling Afghans as they try to put their country back together are daunting. "The biggest thing that's broken in Afghanistan isn't the buildings, or the roads, or even the electrical system. It's the broken psychology," says curator Hiebert. "Twenty-five years of war is hell. Not only were tons of artifacts stolen, so was

"Twenty-five years of war is hell. Not only were tons of artifacts stolen, so was the Afghans' history, their heritage. How can they get their pride back?"

— Fredrik Hiebert
EXHIBITION CURATOR

the Afghans' history, their heritage. Afghan children no longer know Afghan folk songs. How can they get their pride back?"

There are many answers to that question. One is on view in Kabul, where an Afghan national treasure is receiving a makeover. In the early 1500s, the Mogul emperor and famed memoirist Babur laid out a 20-acre garden on a hillside and planted it with his favorite trees. Babur's garden had become an overgrown lot by the time the Aga Khan Trust for Culture began restoring it a few years ago. It is now Kabul's finest public space and a glowing symbol of the tentative, post-Taliban cultural flowering.

At the top of the garden stands Babur's restored white-marble tomb. Not far away, builders have erected a full-scale reproduction of a caravansary, a lodge where Silk Road caravans would spend the night, on precisely the spot where one stood in Babur's day. The day I visited, the caravansary's big courtyard echoed with the sparse, haunting sounds of a traditional stringed instrument known as the sarinda.

The man playing it, Kaka Qader, may be one of the few sarinda masters still alive in Afghanistan. But he won't be the last: A bright-eyed music student watched transfixed as the master played. Then the young man took the instrument, a tabla drummer joined in, and the courtyard resonated with the hopeful sound of a new generation of Afghans playing their music. □

↖ **Treasures on Tour** The National Geographic exhibition will appear in museums in Washington, D.C., San Francisco, Houston, and New York. For venues and dates, visit **ngm.com**.

GOLD HEADDRESS ORNAMENT FROM TILLYA TEPE, 2 IN (5.2 CM) TALL. FIRST CENTURY A.D.

AFGHAN TREASURES 145

Latin America & Antarctica

Latin America incorporates all the regions of the Americas where languages derived from Latin, particularly Spanish and Portuguese, are primarily spoken. South America is the most popular gateway to Antarctica; the Earth's southernmost continent.

Latin America is politically divided into the following countries and territories: Argentina, Bolivia, Brazil, Chile, Colombia, Costa Rica, Cuba, Dominican Republic, Ecuador, El Salvador, Guatemala, Haiti, Honduras, Mexico, Nicaragua, Panama, Paraguay, Peru, Uruguay, Venezuela (Independent Countries) & Puerto Rico. Antarctica does not belong to any country, and has no government; it is considered politically neutral.

Among the new 7 wonders of the world (Voted for in a New Open World Corporation popularity poll), three are in Latin America – the Inca citadel at Machu Picchu in Peru, Christ the Redeemer in Rio de Janeiro and the ancient Maya site of Chichén Itzá in Mexico.

A voyage to Antarctica is an incomparable expedition. The coldest place on Earth, winter temperatures get as low as -70°C, but from November to mid-March temperatures can reach 5°C and this is the optimal time to take a cruise. Cruises are the only way to reach exceptional landscapes like the Ross Ice Shelf and Paradise Harbour. Of course, wildlife is one of the most attractive things about this destination; see endangered albatross, whales and seals. That's not to mention the hundreds of thousands of penguins; a trip to Antarctica guarantees you will see one of the various stages of their life cycle.

For adventurous expeditions to Antarctica between November and March, tall ship "EUROPA" has developed a reputation of a ship that really sails. You are invited to assist the permanent crew in the sail handling by taking the helm, and no experience is required.

Argentina's natural wonders are largely untouched. Trek the Andes which form the country's spine; witness the Jesuit ruins at San Ignacio; watch whales relaxing next to your boat in Patagonia; take in the distinctive capital of Buenos Aires; sample some fine wines in beautiful Mendoza.

Brazil will leave you breathless with its dazzling beaches, jungles, forest trails and vivacious cities. A trip to Rio is a must, but Brazil is much more; visit the North-East which is growing in popularity because of its blend of cultures, cuisine and natural wonders. The Amazon flows from Northern Brazil into the Atlantic and has many places to see Brazil's wilder side, to explore and experience the variety of wildlife.

Brazilian-based tour operator Open Door is one of the main eco-friendly incoming agents for Brazil at present; they promote tours that meet the needs of present tourists by responsible travel to natural areas that conserves the environment and improves the well-being of the local people. Take advantage of their experience when travelling through the "bureaucratic jungles" of Brazil.

A small but beautiful gem in the Andean highlands, Ecuador is dwarfed by its neighbouring countries of Colombia and Peru. The capital city of Quito is a good starting point with its religious monuments and superb architecture. From there, within two hundred miles, a discerning traveller can see the coastal lowlands in the West, the volcanic central highlands, and the rainforests of the East. An island-hop around the Galapagos is an inimitable and memorable experience. The Islands are known for their diversity of wildlife, and visitors can expect a very personal encounter; snorkel with sea lions, walk alongside the giant tortoises and watch iguanas sunbathing.

Explore's tour programme covers the flat desert of Atacama, the lush jungles of Costa Rica, the mountainous terrain of Peru, along with the ancient historical sites of Machu Picchu and Choquequiraoa. Then there are the Latin rhythms of Brazil and Cuba to subsume you too. As the company have been travelling to the South American continent for 26 years, their expertise and knowledge is extensive.

G.A.P Adventures (The Great Adventure People) was recently named the best 'Do It All' Operator on Earth by National Geographic. Their commitment to sustainable and responsible travel is ideal for those who wish to leave the beaten path and authentically engage with local cultures & communities. Whether your adventure is exploring the ruins of Tikal, following the migration of the Hummingbird butterfly in Mexico or volunteering in the Andes, their low-impact, small group approach takes you to the heart of Latin America.

From the tropical beaches of Mexico to the floating ice mountains of the White Continent, Latin America and Antarctica are some of the most diverse, rich and rewarding destinations on the planet.

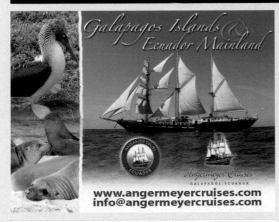

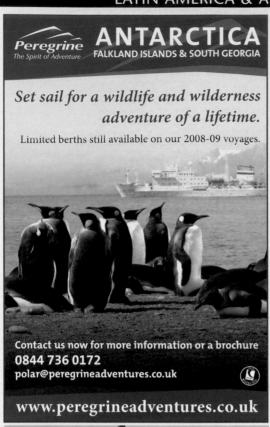

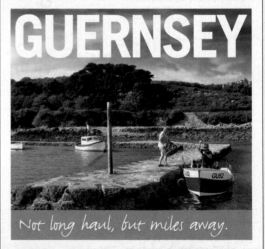

A predator-proofed corral in Ladakh keeps livestock safe from snow leopard attacks.

SNOW LEOPARDS, PAGE 106 **Save the Cats** Covering traditional stone corrals with chain-link fencing (above) protects Himalayan herders' livestock from snow leopards. It also protects snow leopards from the herders themselves. Minimizing livestock losses cuts down on revenge killings of the big cats. Says Darla Hillard of the Snow Leopard Conservancy, which helps fund the predator-proofing, "Our basic approach is to turn the snow leopard from being seen as a pest into a valued asset, worth more alive than dead." The following groups work with Central Asian communities to help both the people who live there and the cats.

■ **Snow Leopard Conservancy** forms partnerships with in-country groups to foster stewardship of snow leopards and their habitat. Efforts include camera traps and tracking with GPS units as well as programs to benefit local people, such as *himalayan-homestays.com*. For more information, go to *snowleopardconservancy.org*.

■ **Snow Leopard Trust** offers an array of conservation programs in five different countries: livestock vaccinations in Pakistan, livestock insurance in India, ecotourism in Kyrgyzstan, and more. Crafts made by Mongolian herder families can be purchased from the trust's Snow Leopard Enterprises at *snowleopard.org/shop*.

THE OLYMPUS E-3 ON ASSIGNMENT

The flagship Olympus E-3 is a camera designed for the most demanding photographers working in the world's most challenging conditions.

Boasting the world's fastest Auto Focus* with an 11-point-full twin cross AF sensor system, together with industry-leading built-in image stabilization that compensates for camera shake by up to 5 EV steps—the Olympus E-3 responds instantly to capture unique moments as they happen.

Ruggedly constructed from rigid magnesium alloy and sealed to keep out dust and splashes, the Olympus E-3 is built to withstand the most severe operating conditions and all the rigors of a relentless professional shooting schedule.

Delivering the highest levels of picture quality, mobility, and reliability—professional photographers choose the Olympus E-3 because world-class photography demands a camera designed for the world.

*Among digital SLR cameras available as of October 17, 2007. When the ZUIKO DIGITAL ED 12-60mm f2.8-4.0 SWD lens is used with the E-3 at a focal length of 60mm (120mm: 35mm equivalent). Based on Olympus's in-house measurement conditions.

COMBAT CLIMATE CHANGE COMPETITION

With today's schoolchildren preparing to face the challenges of climate change, National Geographic is once again harnessing students' ideas for a sustainable solution to lessen its impact. This year's Combat Climate Change competition is being run in association with Swedish energy company Vattenfall and new partner ePals—the largest online global community of connected classrooms.

The competition closes on May 15th, 2008 and is well on the way to receiving many cultural, political, and scientific entries from countries all across Europe. Last year's winning project came from Heta-Elena Heiskanen and Salla-Riina Hokkanen in Finland, who proposed an international energy coalition tackling climate change through schemes including tailored energy-conservation packages to developing countries.

Vattenfall, ePals, and National Geographic strongly encourage you to enter the competition before it closes on May 15th—for details please visit *www.nationalgeographic.com/combatclimatechange*.

INDIA: AN OLD WORLD OF NEW OPPORTUNITIES

India is unique: A land of rich geographical, cultural, and economic contrasts where ancient historical tradition meets modern commercial opportunity. From July 2008 onward, *National Geographic* magazine will introduce a new India-only advertising edition, offering its media partners targeted opportunities in this burgeoning market. *National Geographic* magazine's circulation in India is 25,000 copies (source: ABC June-December 2007).

For more information about *National Geographic* magazine's new India-only advertising edition please contact Marzban Patel at *marzban@media-scope.com*.

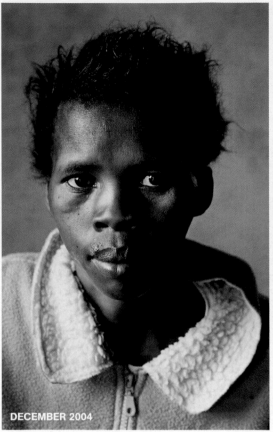

DECEMBER 2004

MARCH 2007

Nompilo Mazuza, now 31, before and after treatment for AIDS and multi-drug-resistant tuberculosis.

UPDATE **Living With AIDS** Nompilo Mazuza (above) was not well when photographer Gideon Mendel first met her in Lusikisiki, South Africa. Her CD4 count, a measure of the immune system, was seven; a count below 200 signals AIDS. She had just started receiving free antiretroviral drugs from a program that Mendel wrote about in the September 2005 *Geographic.* As heard on a multimedia feature from that time on *ngm.com,* Mazuza sounds breathy and exhausted. She says she hopes the antiretroviral drugs will help her. But she also had multi-drug-resistant tuberculosis, which kills many people with AIDS in Africa, and her future was uncertain.

After three years of treatment, Mazuza's CD4 count is 291, and she is TB free. In 2004 a visit to the clinic exhausted her. Now, "I am doing household work, like cleaning the house and fetching water from the river," she says. She would like to start a small business at home, maybe sewing. Most of all, she wants others to look at her and see the power of antiretroviral drugs. She's getting that wish: On a recent clinic visit, she brought a young neighbor with HIV who had seen her get better and hoped the doctors could help him too.

Ken Geiger (above)
wields a flashlight.
Archaeologist Mike
Parker Pearson (below)
excavates a wall.

ON ASSIGNMENT Stonehenge Nights Before senior editor Ken Geiger set out to take pictures of Stonehenge, he knew it would be a challenge to find a fresh way to capture the well-documented site. His solution started with a technique known as light painting. English Heritage granted special access for his all-night photo shoots, which were timed to coincide with the full moon. Dressed entirely in black so as not to become part of the image, Geiger opened the camera's shutter for about 15 minutes and—like a graffiti artist but with a high-intensity flashlight—stopped at each stone to paint it with light. Steady winds on the Salisbury Plain caused drifting clouds to blur, creating shapes and patterns that Geiger never saw until each digital exposure had finished processing. "Every time you shoot," he says, "it's a surprise."

The National Geographic Channel is airing *Stonehenge Decoded* on June 1 at 9 p.m. ET/PT. This new program uses graphics and reenactments to present the ideas Society grantee Mike Parker Pearson has about how Stonehenge might once have been used. And at *ngm.com* readers can explore a three-dimensional photographic model of the megaliths.

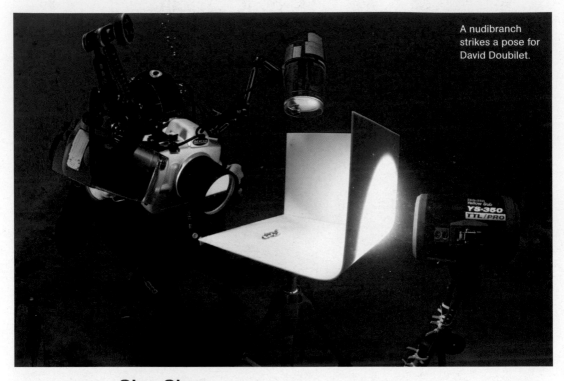

A nudibranch strikes a pose for David Doubilet.

ON ASSIGNMENT Slug Show Many of the nudibranchs on pages 92-105 were photographed right where David Doubilet found them. But some strutted their stuff in a custom-made white mini-studio. Doubilet's idea was to illustrate the nudibranchs' wild colors by separating them from their environment. He set up his gear next to a nudibranch he wanted to photograph, then gently placed it in the studio. "I tried to shoot them like fashion models," he says. All the "models" were returned unharmed.

Bitter cold doesn't stop these crewmen—or photographer Gerd Ludwig (center)—from getting down to work on a Siberian oil rig.

ON ASSIGNMENT
Rigged Up
Photographer Gerd Ludwig was careful where he stood when shooting on rigs for the Siberian oil story. "The work area is fairly small, and you are in people's way all the time," he says. "Often your ideal position blocks their views." Drilling is monotonous and dirty work, and the drill rig is open to the cold sky. Workers spend up to 30 days on the oil pad, miles from the next rig and far from home. But the pay they get is good, says Ludwig—and so is the food.